HOW IT WORKS
BOOK OF
DINOSAURS

Imagine Publishing Ltd
Richmond House
33 Richmond Hill
Bournemouth
Dorset BH2 6EZ
☎ +44 (0) 1202 586200
Website: www.imagine-publishing.co.uk
Twitter: @Books_Imagine
Facebook: www.facebook.com/ImagineBookazines

Publishing Director
Aaron Asadi

Head of Design
Ross Andrews

Production Editor
Hannah Westlake

Senior Art Editor
Greg Whitaker

Designer
David Lewis

Printed by
William Gibbons, 26 Planetary Road, Willenhall, West Midlands, WV13 3XT

Distributed in the UK, Eire & the Rest of the World by
Marketforce, Blue Fin Building, 110 Southwark Street, London, SE1 0SU
Tel 0203 148 3300 www.marketforce.co.uk

Distributed in Australia by
Network Services (a division of Bauer Media Group), Level 21 Civic Tower, 66-68 Goulburn Street,
Sydney, New South Wales 2000, Australia Tel +61 2 8667 5288

ISBN 978-1785 460 678

Part of the
HOW IT WORKS
bookazine series

ip
IMAGINE
PUBLISHING

CONTENTS

066
Biggest dinosaurs

© SPL

© Alamy

© SPL

082
Anatomy of a T-rex

© DK Images

© Thinkstock

© SOL90

THE WORLD'S MOST AMAZING DINOSAURS

Over 500 types of dinosaur existed before they died out 65 million years ago. Here's 26 of the biggest, fiercest and weirdest known to palaeontologists today

Long-lived
T-rex was able to live for up to 30 years

Tyrannosaurus rex
('Tyrant lizard king')

Carnivore

Cretaceous period, 67-66 MYA

Found in: **Western North America**

Lived in: **Forests with swamps and rivers**

Balance
T-rex's huge head was balanced by its heavy tail

Scales or feathers?
T-rex may have had feathers on at least part of its giant body, just like a bird

Fact
The largest T-rex skulls ever to be found are 1.5m across, and some of the T-rex teeth were up to 30cm long

Clawed grip
Although T-rex's arms were small, each with two claws, they were strong, able to grip prey or push itself off the floor

Dino skill

Tyrannosaurus rex

T-rex may have had the most vicious bite of any animal to have lived, many times stronger than lions and sharks and capable of crunching bone and ripping apart its prey.

Killer rating:	5/5
Speed:	3/5
Defence:	3/5

Stegosaurus

('Roof lizard')

Herbivore

Late Jurassic period, 150 MYA

Found in: **Europe and Eastern North America**

Lived in: **Forests and vegetated plains**

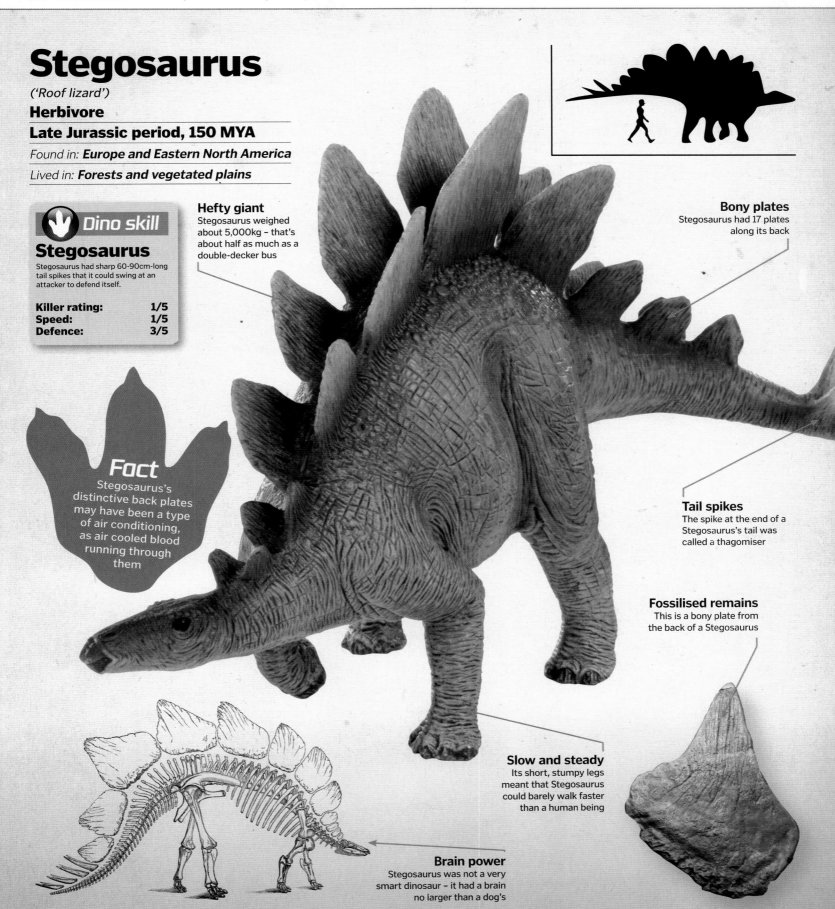

Dino skill

Stegosaurus

Stegosaurus had sharp 60-90cm-long tail spikes that it could swing at an attacker to defend itself.

Killer rating:	1/5
Speed:	1/5
Defence:	3/5

Hefty giant
Stegosaurus weighed about 5,000kg – that's about half as much as a double-decker bus

Fact
Stegosaurus's distinctive back plates may have been a type of air conditioning, as air cooled blood running through them

Bony plates
Stegosaurus had 17 plates along its back

Tail spikes
The spike at the end of a Stegosaurus's tail was called a thagomiser

Fossilised remains
This is a bony plate from the back of a Stegosaurus

Slow and steady
Its short, stumpy legs meant that Stegosaurus could barely walk faster than a human being

Brain power
Stegosaurus was not a very smart dinosaur – it had a brain no larger than a dog's

Triceratops

('Three-horn face')

Herbivore

Late Cretaceous, 67-65 MYA

Found in: **Western North America**

Lived in: **Forests with prairies**

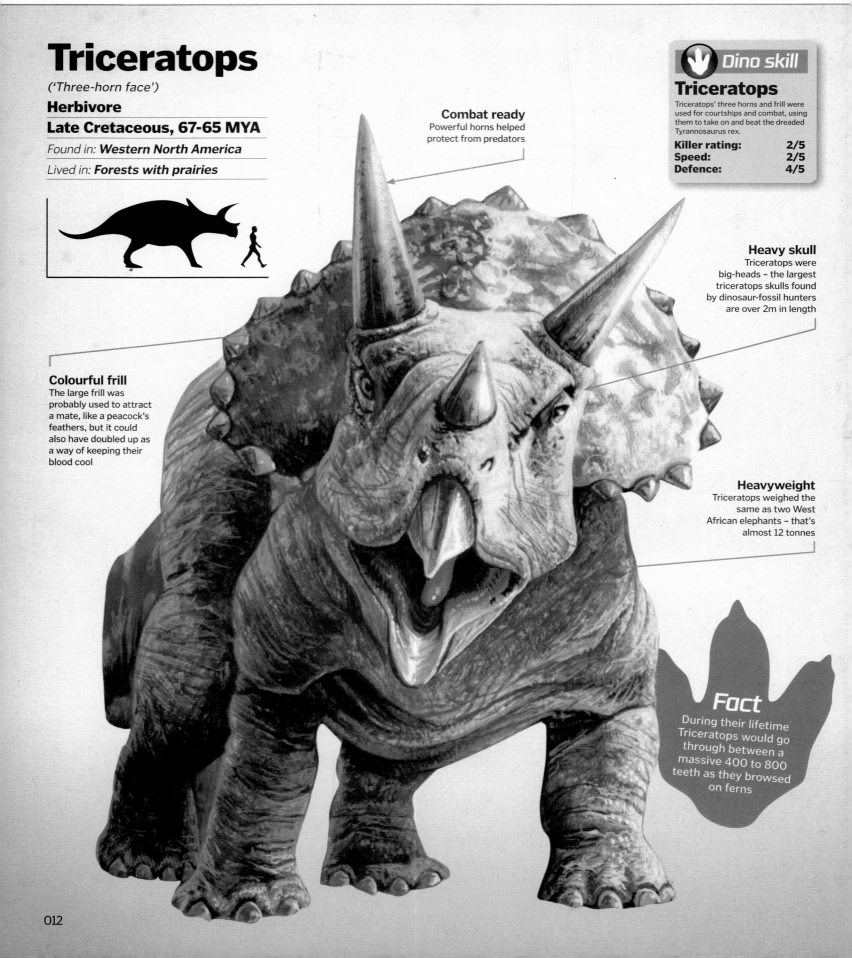

Combat ready
Powerful horns helped protect from predators

Heavy skull
Triceratops were big-heads – the largest triceratops skulls found by dinosaur-fossil hunters are over 2m in length

Colourful frill
The large frill was probably used to attract a mate, like a peacock's feathers, but it could also have doubled up as a way of keeping their blood cool

Heavyweight
Triceratops weighed the same as two West African elephants – that's almost 12 tonnes

Dino skill

Triceratops

Triceratops' three horns and frill were used for courtships and combat, using them to take on and beat the dreaded Tyrannosaurus rex.

Killer rating:	2/5
Speed:	2/5
Defence:	4/5

Fact
During their lifetime Triceratops would go through between a massive 400 to 800 teeth as they browsed on ferns

Velociraptor

('Swift plunderer')

Carnivore

Cretaceous period, 75-71 MYA

Found in: **China, Mongolia**

Lived in: **Desert**

Warm-blooded
Velociraptors were probably warm-blooded

Feathered fiend
Their feathers were used for display, covering nests or providing added speed when running uphill

Fact
In the Jurassic Park films Velociraptors were tall and scaly, but in reality they were more like large birds and were much, much smaller

Small size
Velociraptors were small, like a large chicken

Dino skill

Velociraptor
Velociraptors were loners, hunting other small dinosaurs by launching surprise attacks and then chasing down their prey.

Killer rating:	2/5
Speed:	2/5
Defence:	4/5

Hunting
Their curved claw was a frightening weapon, able to stab and cut open prey

Pounce
They had very strong back legs and sharp claws on their feet

013

Brachiosaurus

('Arm lizard')

Herbivore

Jurassic period, 150 MYA

Found in: **North America**

Lived in: **Forests**

Dino skill

Brachiosaurus

Brachiosaurus just spent its day lumbering around, so wasn't particularly skilful, but it was so large that no predator could harm it.

Killer rating: 1/5
Speed: 1/5
Defence: 4/5

Fact
Brachiosaurus constantly ate. It's thought that it ate between 200 and 400kg of plants every day – that's like eating 400 to 800 lettuces

Foraging
Brachiosaurus may have often held its long neck parallel to the ground to sift through the undergrowth for food, as well as to reach up to leaves on trees

Small skull
Brachiosaurus had a tiny head

Earth-shaker
Adult Brachiosaurus weighed over 100 tonnes

Vertebra
This is a bone from the long neck of the Brachiosaurus called a vertebra

Extra height
Unlike many other dinosaurs, their front legs were longer than their back legs, which provided additional elevation for their neck and head

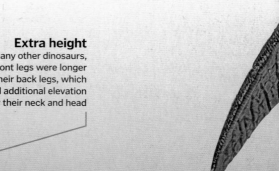

Pteranodon
('Toothless wing')

Carnivore

Late Cretaceous, 88-80 MYA

Found in: **North America**

Lived in: **Coastal/lake areas**

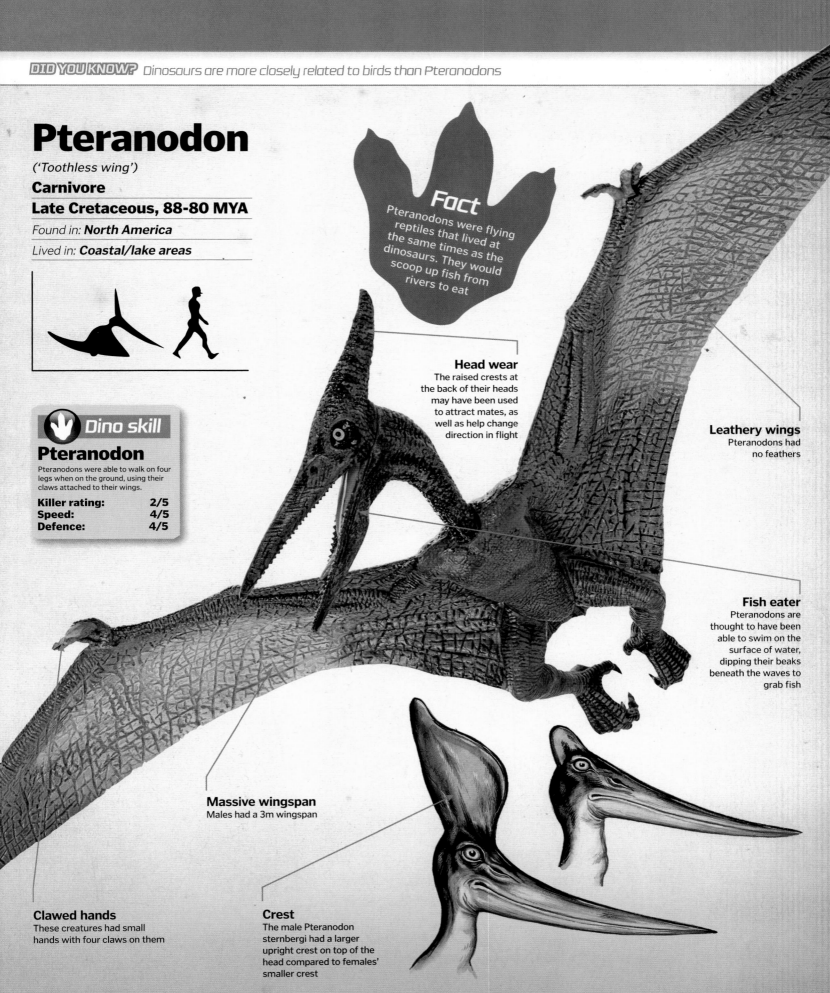

Dino skill

Pteranodon

Pteranodons were able to walk on four legs when on the ground, using their claws attached to their wings.

Killer rating:	2/5
Speed:	4/5
Defence:	4/5

Fact
Pteranodons were flying reptiles that lived at the same times as the dinosaurs. They would scoop up fish from rivers to eat

Head wear
The raised crests at the back of their heads may have been used to attract mates, as well as help change direction in flight

Leathery wings
Pteranodons had no feathers

Fish eater
Pteranodons are thought to have been able to swim on the surface of water, dipping their beaks beneath the waves to grab fish

Massive wingspan
Males had a 3m wingspan

Clawed hands
These creatures had small hands with four claws on them

Crest
The male Pteranodon sternbergi had a larger upright crest on top of the head compared to females' smaller crest

Allosaurus

('Different lizard')

Carnivore

Late Jurassic, 155-150 MYA

Found in: **North America**

Lived in: **Semi-arid plains and forests**

Dino skill

Allosaurus

Allosaurus was able to sniff out its prey, like Stegosaurus and Diplodocus, with a keen sense of smell.

Killer rating:	4/5
Speed:	4/5
Defence:	4/5

Eyesight
Forward-facing eyes helped focus on prey

Keeping balance
Its large and terrifying skull was balanced by its heavy tail, so that it didn't fall forward all the time

Jaw strength
Its mighty jaws could clamp down hard on its prey, but not as hard as an alligator, for example

Fact
Allosaurus' backward-facing, 10cm-long teeth meant that it could continuously push its prey further down its mouth

Claws
Razor-sharp claws

Allosaurus skull
This is what the skull of an Allosaurus looks like

Shorter stride
Their legs weren't as long as a Tyrannosaur's and they couldn't run as fast

Spinosaurus
('Spine lizard')
Carnivore
Cretaceous period, 112-97 MYA
Found in: **North Africa**
Lived in: **Forests**

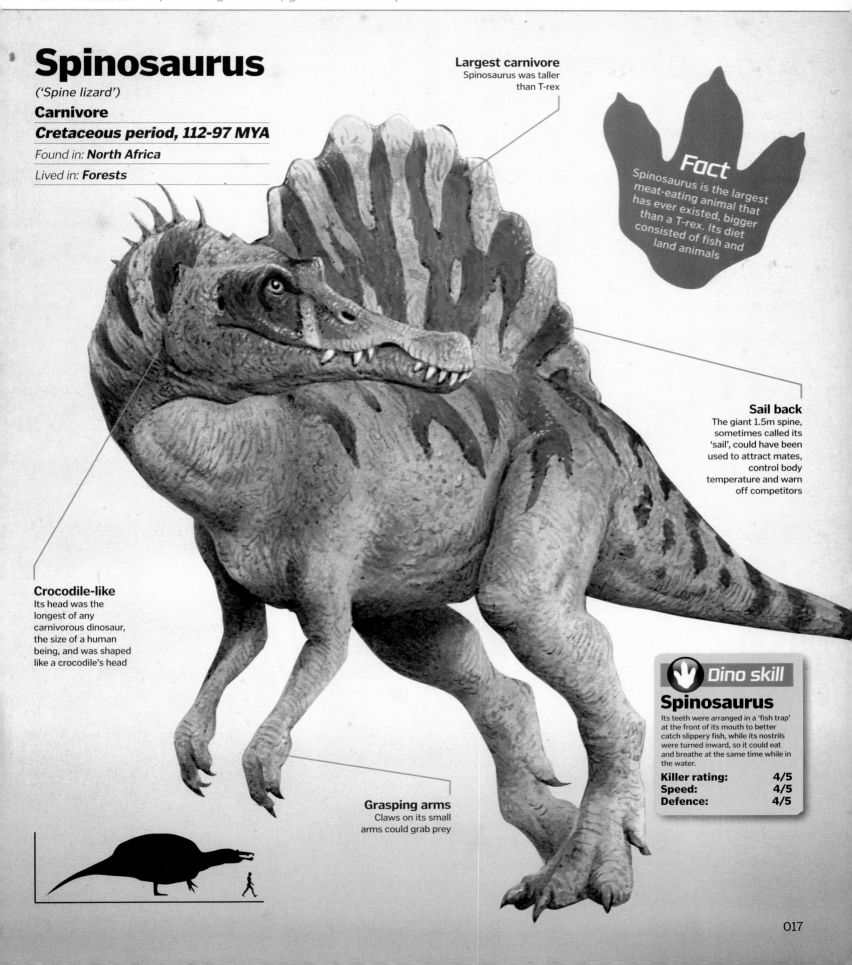

Largest carnivore
Spinosaurus was taller than T-rex

Fact
Spinosaurus is the largest meat-eating animal that has ever existed, bigger than a T-rex. Its diet consisted of fish and land animals

Sail back
The giant 1.5m spine, sometimes called its 'sail', could have been used to attract mates, control body temperature and warn off competitors

Crocodile-like
Its head was the longest of any carnivorous dinosaur, the size of a human being, and was shaped like a crocodile's head

Grasping arms
Claws on its small arms could grab prey

Dino skill

Spinosaurus
Its teeth were arranged in a 'fish trap' at the front of its mouth to better catch slippery fish, while its nostrils were turned inward, so it could eat and breathe at the same time while in the water.

Killer rating:	4/5
Speed:	4/5
Defence:	4/5

Argentinosaurus

('Argentine lizard')

Herbivore

Cretaceous, 95 MYA

Found in: **Argentina**

Lived in: **Forests**

Egg production
Adult Argentinosaurs would lay dozens of eggs each year

Armoured
We can tell from fossil finds that its skin was armoured

Intelligence
Its small brain meant that Argentinosaurus was not particularly intelligent

Slow mover
Argentinosaurus was incredibly slow and walked at 8km/h – a human could beat it in a walking race

Manure
Argentinosaurus would have produced 15 litres' worth of dino droppings each time – that's about five big buckets of poo in one go

Fact
Argentinosaurus was the largest animal to walk the Earth. Babies had to grow a massive 25,000 times their original size

Dino skill

Argentinosaurus

Argentinosaurus had the ability to stand up on its back legs, then come crashing down on any attackers.

Killer rating:	2/5
Speed:	1/5
Defence:	3/5

Carnotaurus

('Meat-eating bull')

Carnivore

Late Cretaceous, 70 MYA

Found in: **Argentina**

Lived in: **Lake environments**

Poor vision
Carnotaurus had small eyes, so its vision was not very good. Combined with not being able to turn easily, it probably just smashed through obstacles

Fact
Carnotaurus could run very fast, faster than the T-rex, but it could not turn very well, so it tended to charge prey in straight lines

Searching smell
It used its sense of smell to hunt

Scaly hide
Carnotaurus' scales were small and pebble-like

Dino skill

Carnotaurus

With the horns on its forehead and muscular neck, Carnotaurus could head-butt its prey into submission.

Killer rating:	5/5
Speed:	4/5
Defence:	4/5

Strong thighs
Carnotaurus had powerful thigh muscles that were so big they weighed twice as much as a human being. The Carnotaurus as a whole weighed the same as a small car

Skull
The skull of a Carnotaurus

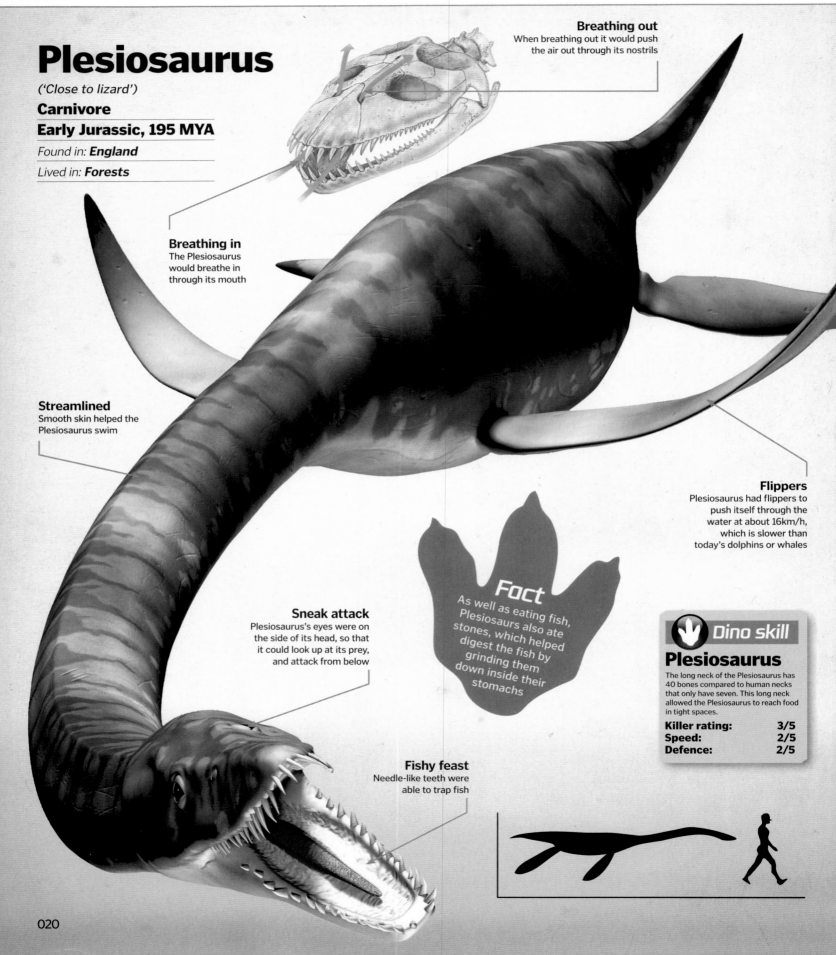

Plesiosaurus

('Close to lizard')

Carnivore

Early Jurassic, 195 MYA

Found in: **England**

Lived in: **Forests**

Breathing out
When breathing out it would push the air out through its nostrils

Breathing in
The Plesiosaurus would breathe in through its mouth

Streamlined
Smooth skin helped the Plesiosaurus swim

Flippers
Plesiosaurus had flippers to push itself through the water at about 16km/h, which is slower than today's dolphins or whales

Sneak attack
Plesiosaurus's eyes were on the side of its head, so that it could look up at its prey, and attack from below

Fact
As well as eating fish, Plesiosaurs also ate stones, which helped digest the fish by grinding them down inside their stomachs

Fishy feast
Needle-like teeth were able to trap fish

Dino skill

Plesiosaurus

The long neck of the Plesiosaurus has 40 bones compared to human necks that only have seven. This long neck allowed the Plesiosaurus to reach food in tight spaces.

Killer rating:	3/5
Speed:	2/5
Defence:	2/5

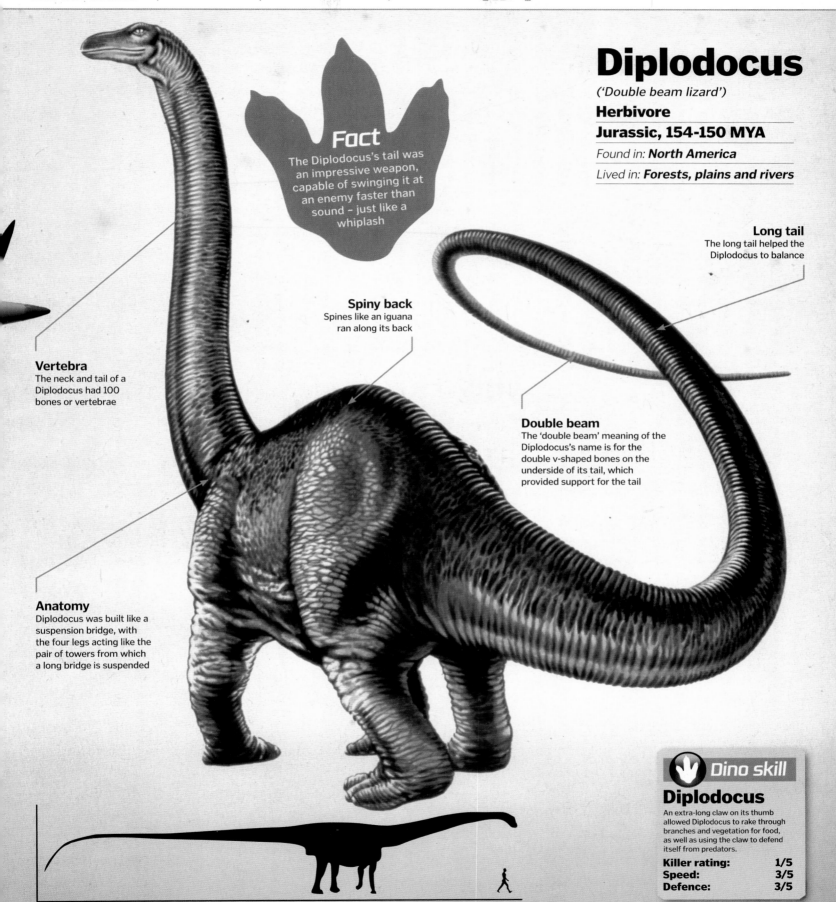

Fact
The Diplodocus's tail was an impressive weapon, capable of swinging it at an enemy faster than sound – just like a whiplash

Diplodocus

('Double beam lizard')

Herbivore

Jurassic, 154-150 MYA

Found in: **North America**

Lived in: **Forests, plains and rivers**

Long tail
The long tail helped the Diplodocus to balance

Spiny back
Spines like an iguana ran along its back

Vertebra
The neck and tail of a Diplodocus had 100 bones or vertebrae

Double beam
The 'double beam' meaning of the Diplodocus's name is for the double v-shaped bones on the underside of its tail, which provided support for the tail

Anatomy
Diplodocus was built like a suspension bridge, with the four legs acting like the pair of towers from which a long bridge is suspended

Dino skill

Diplodocus

An extra-long claw on its thumb allowed Diplodocus to rake through branches and vegetation for food, as well as using the claw to defend itself from predators.

Killer rating:	**1/5**
Speed:	**3/5**
Defence:	**3/5**

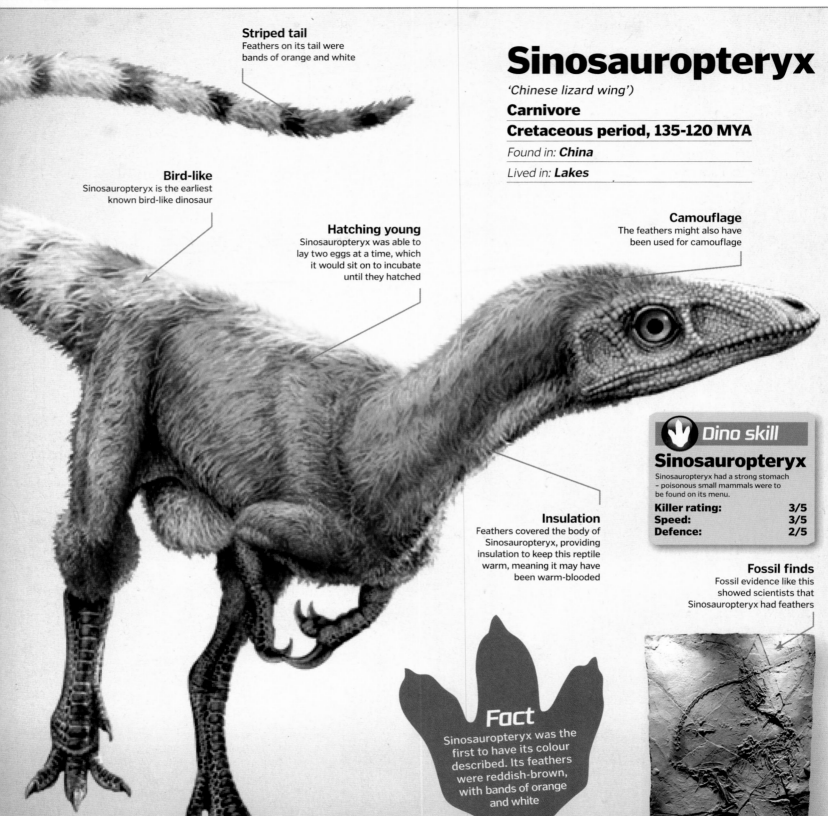

Striped tail
Feathers on its tail were bands of orange and white

Sinosauropteryx

'Chinese lizard wing'

Carnivore

Cretaceous period, 135-120 MYA

Found in: **China**

Lived in: **Lakes**

Bird-like
Sinosauropteryx is the earliest known bird-like dinosaur

Hatching young
Sinosauropteryx was able to lay two eggs at a time, which it would sit on to incubate until they hatched

Camouflage
The feathers might also have been used for camouflage

Insulation
Feathers covered the body of Sinosauropteryx, providing insulation to keep this reptile warm, meaning it may have been warm-blooded

Dino skill

Sinosauropteryx

Sinosauropteryx had a strong stomach – poisonous small mammals were to be found on its menu.

Killer rating:	3/5
Speed:	3/5
Defence:	2/5

Fossil finds
Fossil evidence like this showed scientists that Sinosauropteryx had feathers

Fact
Sinosauropteryx was the first to have its colour described. Its feathers were reddish-brown, with bands of orange and white

Ankylosaurus

('Fused lizard')

Herbivore

Cretaceous, 70-65 MYA

Found in: **South America**

Lived in: **Coastal plains**

Spiky defence
Two rows of spikes ran along its body, plus there were two large horns from the back of its head that it could defend itself with

Small brained
The Ankylosaurus had a small brain

Fact
Ankylosaurus was built like a tank and had strong plates of bone fused into the skin on its back that was impenetrable to even T-rex

Breaking bones
Powerful club-tail could break an attacker's bones

Early impression
This is an old sketch of an Ankylosaur's skeleton, before the tail club was discovered

Five-toed
Ankylosaurus probably had five toes on each foot

Vulnerable
The underside of its belly was the only place the Ankylosaurus was not armoured – flipping it over was the only way to kill it

Bone head
Its entire head was covered in bony plates

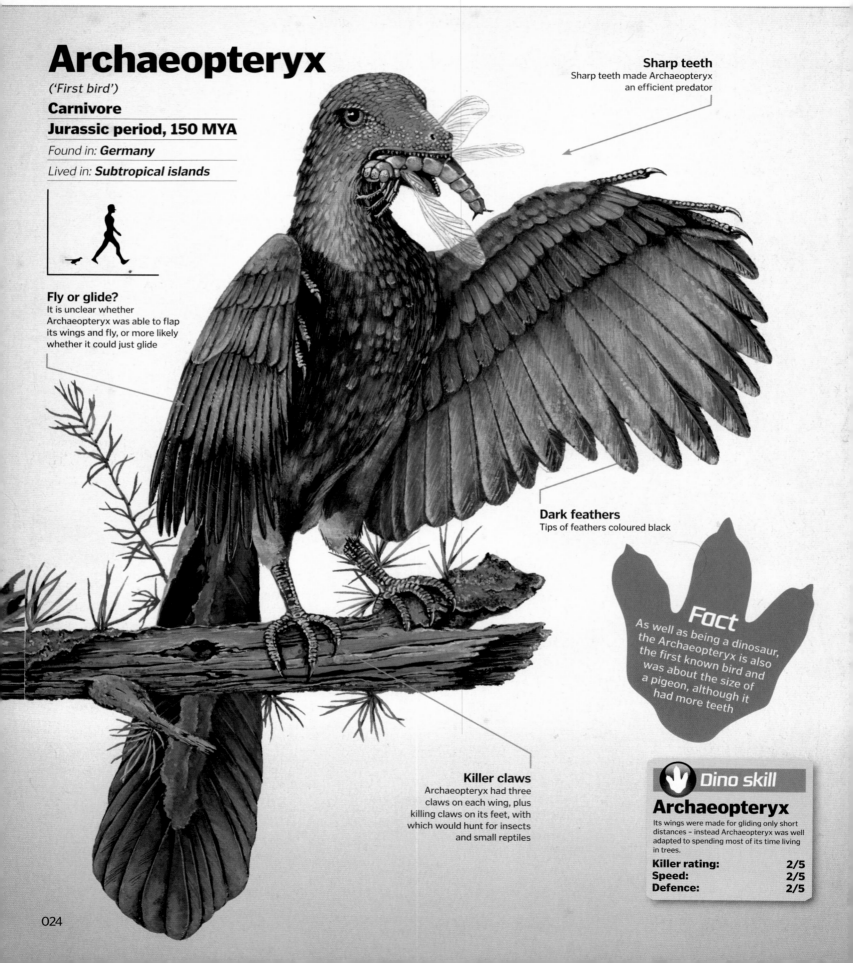

Archaeopteryx

('First bird')

Carnivore

Jurassic period, 150 MYA

Found in: **Germany**

Lived in: **Subtropical islands**

Sharp teeth
Sharp teeth made Archaeopteryx an efficient predator

Fly or glide?
It is unclear whether Archaeopteryx was able to flap its wings and fly, or more likely whether it could just glide

Dark feathers
Tips of feathers coloured black

Fact
As well as being a dinosaur, the Archaeopteryx is also the first known bird and was about the size of a pigeon, although it had more teeth

Killer claws
Archaeopteryx had three claws on each wing, plus killing claws on its feet, with which would hunt for insects and small reptiles

Dino skill

Archaeopteryx

Its wings were made for gliding only short distances – instead Archaeopteryx was well adapted to spending most of its time living in trees.

Killer rating:	2/5
Speed:	2/5
Defence:	2/5

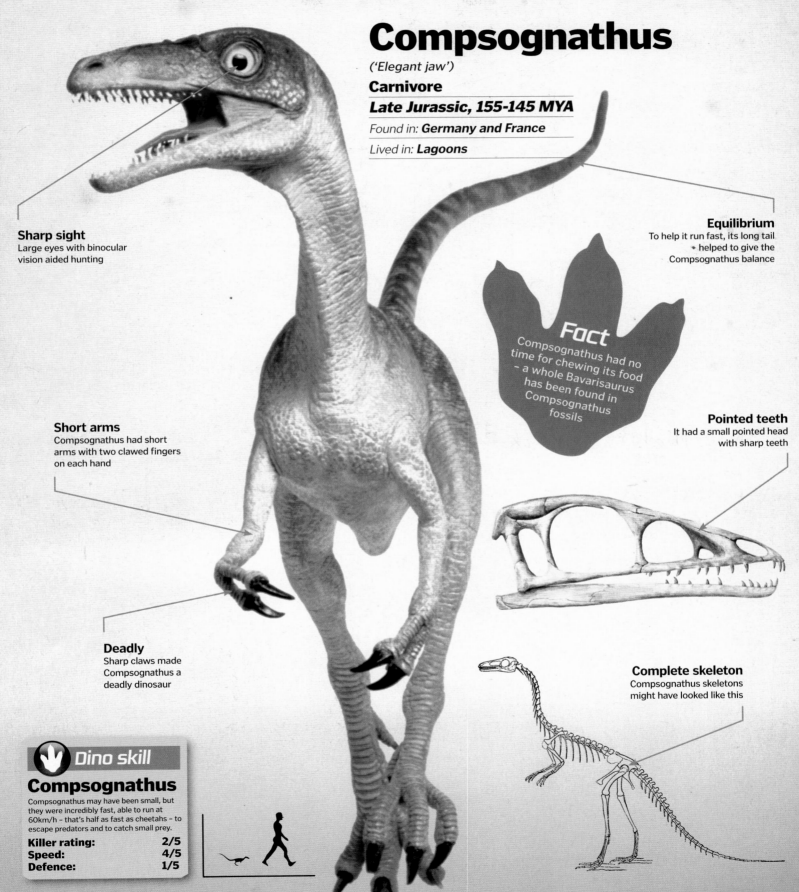

Compsognathus

('Elegant jaw')

Carnivore

Late Jurassic, 155-145 MYA

Found in: **Germany and France**

Lived in: **Lagoons**

Sharp sight
Large eyes with binocular vision aided hunting

Equilibrium
To help it run fast, its long tail helped to give the Compsognathus balance

Fact
Compsognathus had no time for chewing its food – a whole Bavarisaurus has been found in Compsognathus fossils

Short arms
Compsognathus had short arms with two clawed fingers on each hand

Pointed teeth
It had a small pointed head with sharp teeth

Deadly
Sharp claws made Compsognathus a deadly dinosaur

Complete skeleton
Compsognathus skeletons might have looked like this

Dino skill

Compsognathus

Compsognathus may have been small, but they were incredibly fast, able to run at 60km/h – that's half as fast as cheetahs – to escape predators and to catch small prey.

Killer rating:	**2/5**
Speed:	**4/5**
Defence:	**1/5**

Herrerasaurus

('Herrera's lizard')

Carnivore

Late Triassic, 231 MYA

Found in: **Argentina**

Lived in: **River floodplains with active volcanoes**

Dino skill

Herrerasaurus

One of the first dinosaurs, Herrerasaurus had an semi-opposable thumb among its claws, allowing it to grab more firmly onto its prey

Killer rating:	4/5
Speed:	4/5
Defence:	2/5

Deadly grip
Inwardly curving teeth allowed it to hang onto its prey

Grasping jaws
Its lower jaw was jointed, allowing it to slide back and forth to grasp and bite prey

Long reach
Longer arms than T-rex or Allosaurus

Fact
Compared to T-rex, Herrerasaurus is tiny. It lived in a time when all dinos were fairly small, meaning it was a top predator

Sawing bite
It could slide its lower jaw forward and backward in a sawing bite

Big feet
Herrerasaurus had big feet, which, along with its strong legs and powerful thigh muscles, meant it could gallop quite fast, up to 40km/h

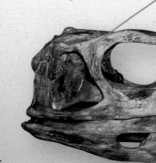

Pachycephalosaurus

('Thick-headed lizard')

Herbivore

Late Cretaceous, 65-75 MYA

Found in: **North America, Isle of Wight, Mongolia, Madagascar**

Lived in: **Coastal regions**

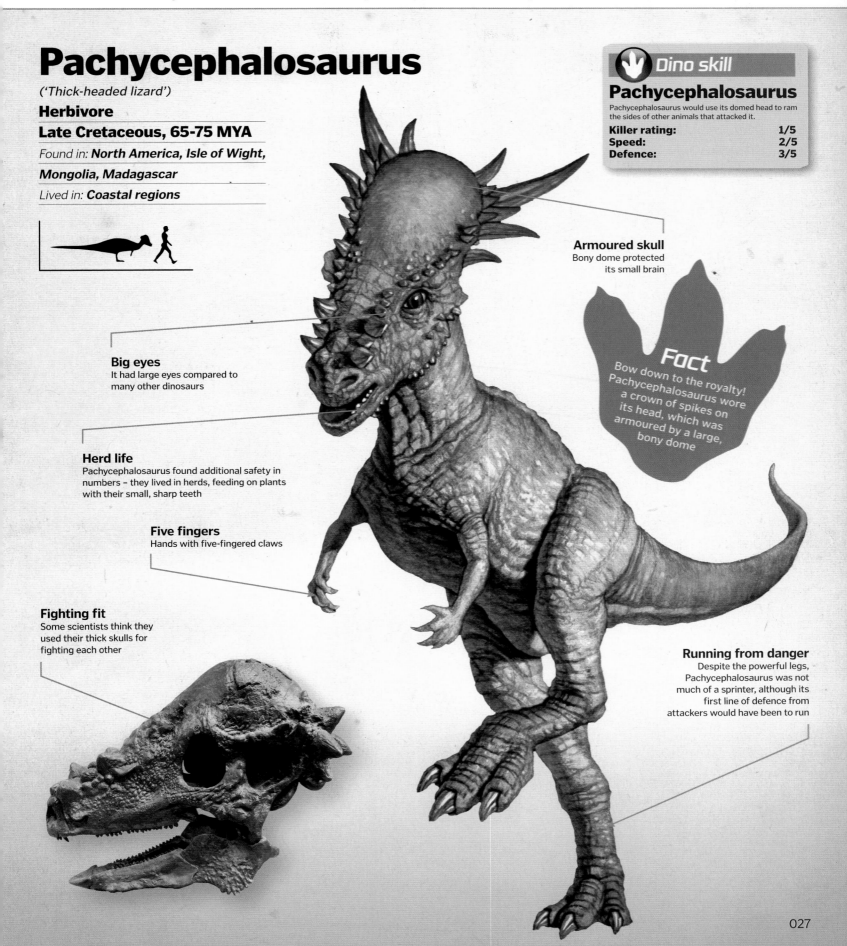

Dino skill

Pachycephalosaurus

Pachycephalosaurus would use its domed head to ram the sides of other animals that attacked it.

Killer rating:	1/5
Speed:	2/5
Defence:	3/5

Armoured skull
Bony dome protected its small brain

Big eyes
It had large eyes compared to many other dinosaurs

Herd life
Pachycephalosaurus found additional safety in numbers – they lived in herds, feeding on plants with their small, sharp teeth

Five fingers
Hands with five-fingered claws

Fighting fit
Some scientists think they used their thick skulls for fighting each other

Fact
Bow down to the royalty! Pachycephalosaurus wore a crown of spikes on its head, which was armoured by a large, bony dome

Running from danger
Despite the powerful legs, Pachycephalosaurus was not much of a sprinter, although its first line of defence from attackers would have been to run

027

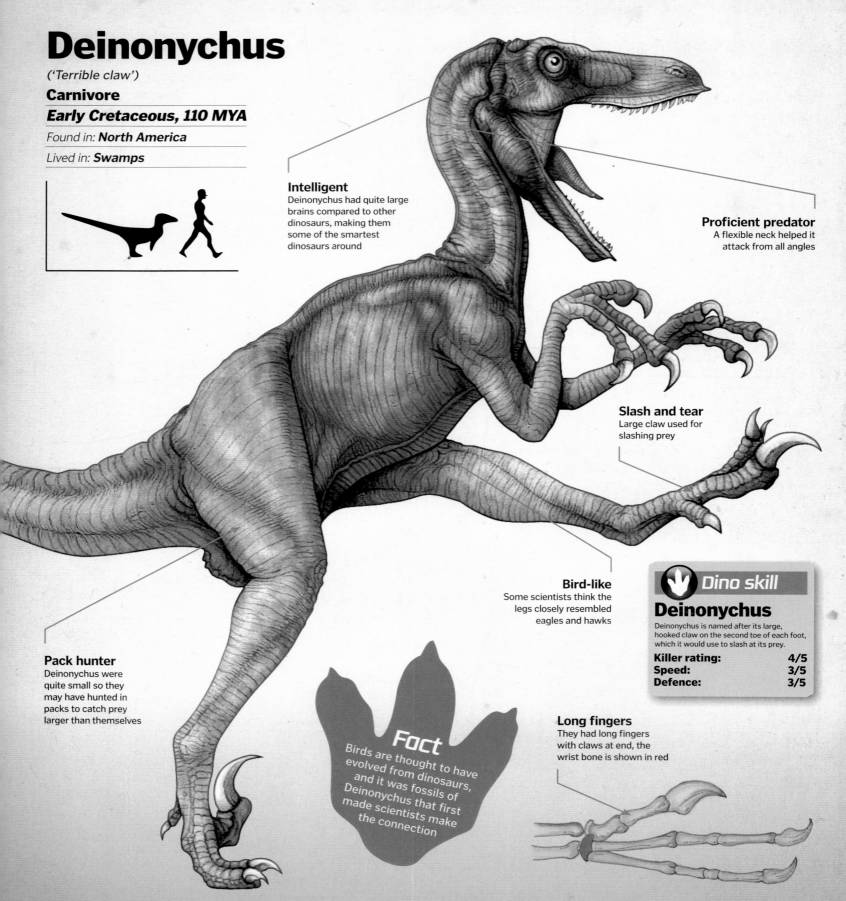

Deinonychus

('Terrible claw')

Carnivore

Early Cretaceous, 110 MYA

Found in: **North America**

Lived in: **Swamps**

Intelligent
Deinonychus had quite large brains compared to other dinosaurs, making them some of the smartest dinosaurs around

Proficient predator
A flexible neck helped it attack from all angles

Slash and tear
Large claw used for slashing prey

Bird-like
Some scientists think the legs closely resembled eagles and hawks

Pack hunter
Deinonychus were quite small so they may have hunted in packs to catch prey larger than themselves

Fact
Birds are thought to have evolved from dinosaurs, and it was fossils of Deinonychus that first made scientists make the connection

Long fingers
They had long fingers with claws at end, the wrist bone is shown in red

Dino skill

Deinonychus

Deinonychus is named after its large, hooked claw on the second toe of each foot, which it would use to slash at its prey.

Killer rating:	4/5
Speed:	3/5
Defence:	3/5

Liopleurodon
('Smooth-sided teeth')

Carnivore

Mid-Jurassic, 160-155 MYA

Found in: **Europe**

Lived in: **The sea**

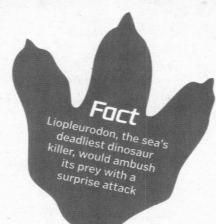

Fact

Liopleurodon, the sea's deadliest dinosaur killer, would ambush its prey with a surprise attack

Dino skill

Liopleurodon

In the dark seas of the Jurassic era, the Liopleurodon used its keen sense of smell to sniff out prey that had the misfortune to swim past it.

Killer rating:	4/5
Speed:	3/5
Defence:	0/5

Sharp teeth
Teeth as big and sharp as kitchen knives would crunch down on prey

Heavyweight
Liopleurodon weighed 2.5 tonnes – that's about the same as 13 dolphins

Flippers
The rear two flippers were larger than the front

Speed
The Liopleurodon's four flippers propelled it through the water, but not very fast, swimming at only 10kmh

Super size
The Liopleurodon was longer than a sperm whale

Euoplocephalus

('Well-armed head')

Herbivore

Late Cretaceous, 70 MYA

Found in: **North America**

Lived in: **Forests and rivers**

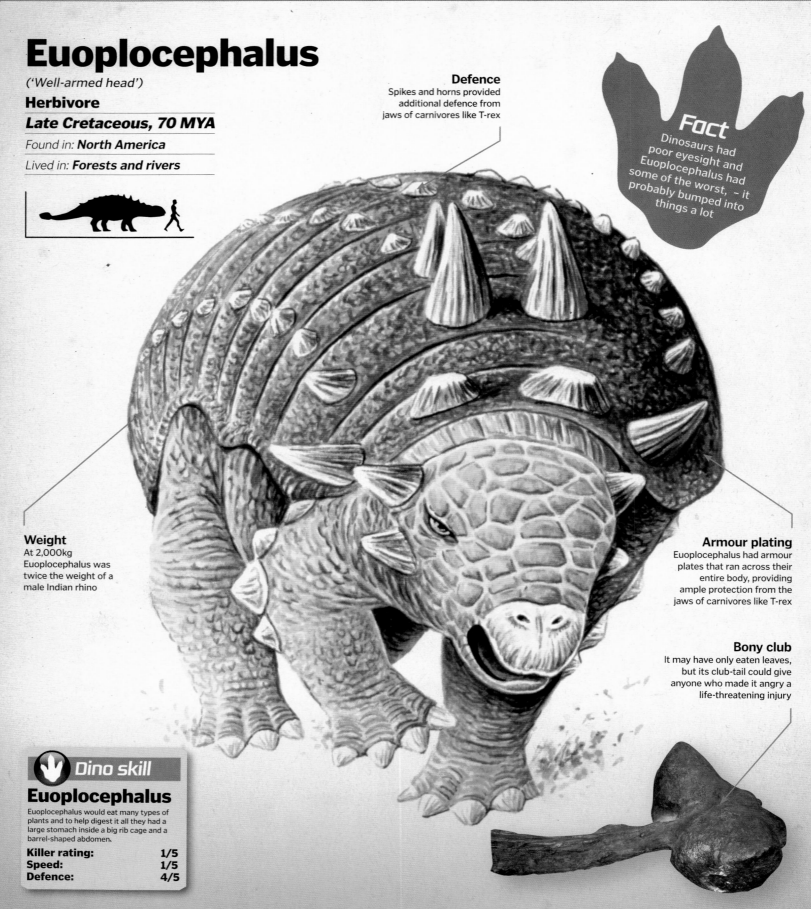

Defence
Spikes and horns provided additional defence from jaws of carnivores like T-rex

Fact
Dinosaurs had poor eyesight and Euoplocephalus had some of the worst, – it probably bumped into things a lot

Weight
At 2,000kg Euoplocephalus was twice the weight of a male Indian rhino

Armour plating
Euoplocephalus had armour plates that ran across their entire body, providing ample protection from the jaws of carnivores like T-rex

Bony club
It may have only eaten leaves, but its club-tail could give anyone who made it angry a life-threatening injury

Dino skill

Euoplocephalus

Euoplocephalus would eat many types of plants and to help digest it all they had a large stomach inside a big rib cage and a barrel-shaped abdomen.

Killer rating:	1/5
Speed:	1/5
Defence:	4/5

Intelligence
Giganotosaurus was not very smart – its brain was small, and banana-shaped

Gigantosaurus
('Giant southern lizard')

Carnivore

Cretaceous period, 100 MYA

Found in: **South America**

Lived in: **Argentina**

Serrated teeth
Giganotosaurus would have given T-rex a run for its money, being larger, with serrated knife-like teeth for cutting into prey

Fact
Despite being huge, Giganotosaurus would often fall over when running fast because it would lose balance at speed

Claws
It had short but powerful arms with razor-sharp claws on each hand

High speeds
Giganotosaurus could run at the same speed as a car in a 30mph zone

Big predator
Giganotosaurus weighed up to eight tonnes

☝ Dino skill

Gigantosaurus

Its thin, pointed tail would have provided balance, allowing the Giganotosaurus to turn quickly, making it agile enough to catch difficult prey.

Killer rating:	4/5
Speed:	3/5
Defence:	3/5

Iguanodon

('Iguana-tooth')

Herbivore

Early Cretaceous, 130 MYA

Found in: **Europe, North America, Africa, Asia**

Lived in: **Forests, plains and rivers**

Dino skill

Iguanodon

The Iguanodon's claws also had a thumb spike, which could have been used to help grab food, as well as fend off any attackers that got too close.

Killer rating:	1/5
Speed:	3/5
Defence:	2/5

Fact
Most dinosaurs stayed in one region but Iguanodons spent a lot of time moving, to all continents except Antarctica

Tail
Iguanodon had a long, stiff tail

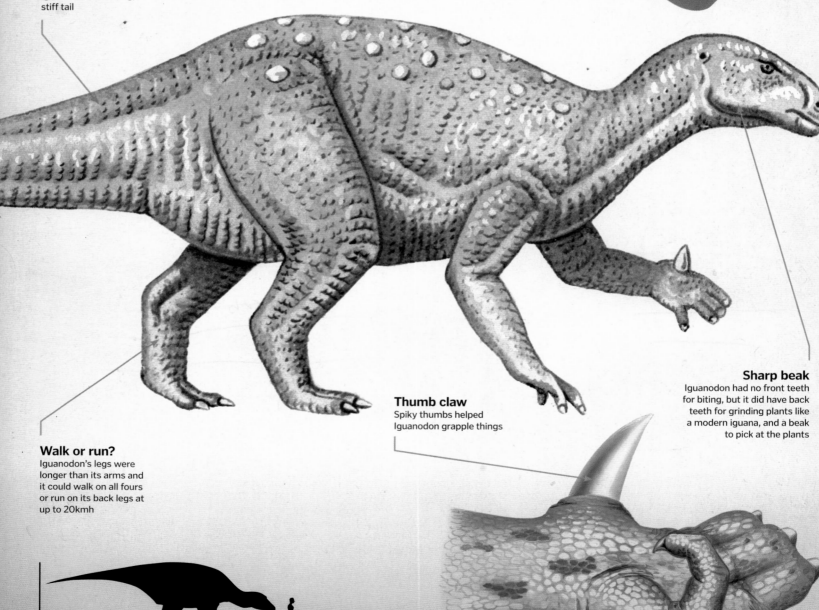

Walk or run?
Iguanodon's legs were longer than its arms and it could walk on all fours or run on its back legs at up to 20kmh

Thumb claw
Spiky thumbs helped Iguanodon grapple things

Sharp beak
Iguanodon had no front teeth for biting, but it did have back teeth for grinding plants like a modern iguana, and a beak to pick at the plants

Seismosaurus

('Quake lizard')

Herbivore

Late Jurassic, 156-145 MYA

Found in: **North America**

Lived in: **Forests, plains and rivers**

 **Dino skill**

Seismosaurus

Its long neck ended in a small head armed
with peg-like teeth that could strip entire
woodlands of their leaves and other foliage
in no time at all!

Killer rating:	1/5
Speed:	1/5
Defence:	4/5

Fact
Seismosaurus is a giant
version of the Diplodocus.
The ground would
literally have shaken
when this beast
lumbered past

Long reach
A long neck allowed
Seismosaurus to reach food

Herding instinct
Seismosaurus travelled in
grazing herds

Sturdy legs
Its enormous weight
meant Seismosaurus
needed very strong and
sturdy legs to hold it up

Whip-like tail
Its long tail was a deadly
weapon to be used against
any would-be attackers

Ouranosaurus

('Brave lizard')

Herbivore

Early Cretaceous, 115-110 MYA

Found in: **North Africa**

Lived in: **Forests**

Intelligence
Ouranosaurus had average intelligence for a dinosaur

Sail
The distinctive spine ran across the length of Ouranosaurus' back and besides keeping the dinosaur cool, could have stored energy for the winter

Dino skill

Ouranosaurus
Like Spinosaurus and Stegosaurus, the large sail on the spine of Ouranosaurus helped to regulate its temperature.

Killer rating:	1/5
Speed:	2/5
Defence:	2/5

Herbivore
Ouranosaurus had no teeth in its beak, but it had teeth inside its cheeks, with which it chewed up food such as leaves, fruit and seeds

Two legs or four?
Ouranosaurus could run on two legs or walk on four

Skull
Its skull was 67cm long and quite flat

Fact
Ouranosaurus did not have many defence mechanisms but it could use its sail to appear bigger than it really was to enemies

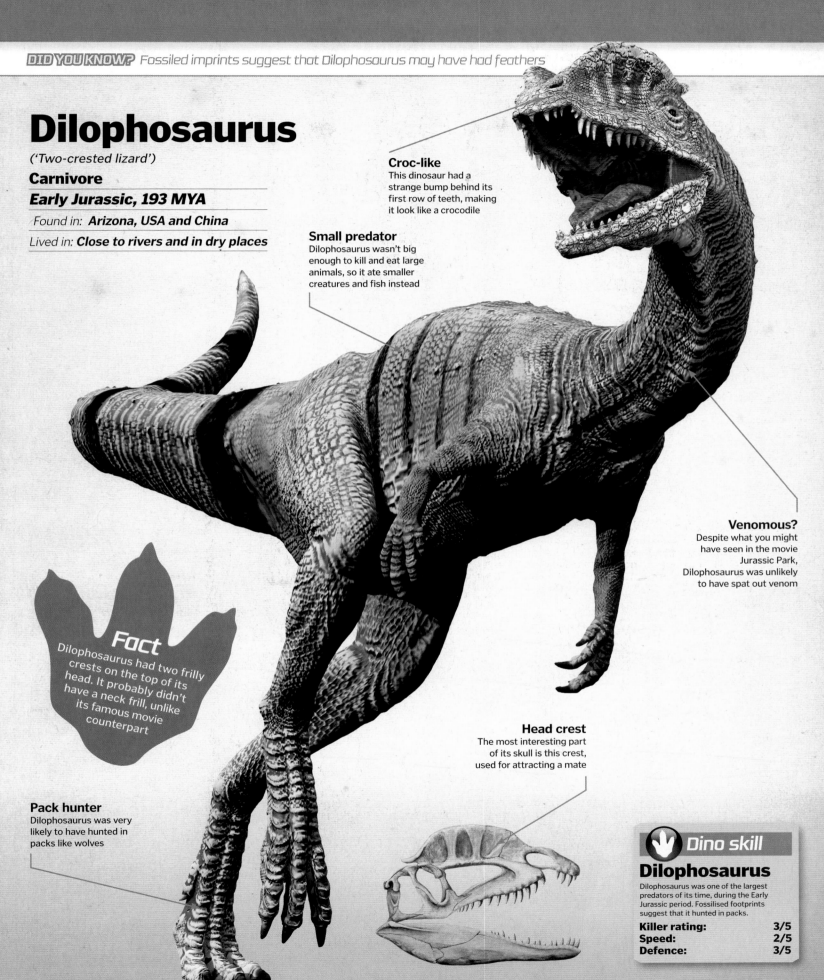

Dilophosaurus

('Two-crested lizard')

Carnivore

Early Jurassic, 193 MYA

Found in: **Arizona, USA and China**

Lived in: **Close to rivers and in dry places**

Croc-like
This dinosaur had a strange bump behind its first row of teeth, making it look like a crocodile

Small predator
Dilophosaurus wasn't big enough to kill and eat large animals, so it ate smaller creatures and fish instead

Venomous?
Despite what you might have seen in the movie Jurassic Park, Dilophosaurus was unlikely to have spat out venom

Fact
Dilophosaurus had two frilly crests on the top of its head. It probably didn't have a neck frill, unlike its famous movie counterpart

Pack hunter
Dilophosaurus was very likely to have hunted in packs like wolves

Head crest
The most interesting part of its skull is this crest, used for attracting a mate

Dino skill

Dilophosaurus

Dilophosaurus was one of the largest predators of its time, during the Early Jurassic period. Fossilised footprints suggest that it hunted in packs.

Killer rating:	3/5
Speed:	2/5
Defence:	3/5

HOW IT WORKS BOOK OF DINOSAURS

THE PREHISTORIC WORLD

The prehistoric world

041
Mass
destruction

045
Meteor
impact

054
Jurassic swamps

© DK Images

042
Tyrant lizard king

040
Dinosaur communication

© Corbis Images

056
Jurassic ocean

058
Cretaceous plains

A to Z of the dinosaurs

From birth to extinction, get to know these prehistoric beasts inside and out with our comprehensive A-Z guide

 Dinosaurs have long sparked our imagination. From the Ancient Greeks' perception of their remains as evidence of a time when giants ruled Earth, right through to modern man's pursuit of their resurrection – be that in films like Jurassic Park or in laboratories via advanced DNA cloning techniques – dinosaurs remain a tantalisingly alien part of our world's history.

They may no longer roam the land like they did millions of years ago, but thanks to their genetic legacy and preserved remains they still remain a very real presence today.

From the fossils lying trapped in the ground through to the descendants flying above our heads, dinosaurs have unique tales to tell.

We take a closer look at this ancient world through an A-Z encyclopedia of all things dinosaur. You'll learn not just about the creatures themselves but the tools and techniques used to study them, and what Earth was like during their reign. This guide truly has it all, so strap yourself in and prepare for one wild, prehistoric ride...

Benton on a fossil dig near Albuquerque, New Mexico

 **Professor Mike Benton, palaeontologist**
Mike Benton is the Professor of Vertebrate Palaeontology at the University of Bristol, UK, and is a world-renowned dinosaur specialist. His areas of expertise include the diversification of life through time, the origin of dinosaurs and the end-Permian mass-extinction event. He can be found working on digs in Russia and China. He offers words of wisdom throughout our dino guide, but for a more in-depth interview, head to **howitworksdaily.com**.

Amber & dino DNA

Amber is fossilised tree resin that, due to a chemical change after burial in the ground, turns into a solid. Despite its stable state today, when the majority of the Earth's amber formed, it was far more fluid, which means many little organisms unwittingly became stuck within it – including plant matter and insects. Today these appear frozen within the amber and have been perfectly preserved. While one or two studies in the Nineties claimed to extract DNA from these organic inclusions (as portrayed in Jurassic Park), more recent research suggests this isn't possible. Scientists at the University of Manchester using advanced DNA sequencing in 2013 were not even able to find traces of DNA in copal (a precursor to amber) only 10,000 years old, so they're very doubtful that dino DNA could have survived from millions of years ago.

Communication in focus

Dinosaurs, much like the many species of animal alive today, communicated in very different ways. From complex dance-like movements to more obvious calls and scent markings, each dino marked their territory, warned of potential predators and relayed information regarding food in its own unique way. One of the most interesting examples comes in the form of the hadrosaurid (above), a duck-billed dinosaur family sporting a distinctive bone crest on their heads. These crests were used as a resonating chamber for projecting their calls. Considering the hadrosaur's modest size and its wide range of predators, the ability to amplify its calls was no doubt a valuable defensive mechanism.

"Certain kinds of excavation and study out in the field can be for palaeoecology, trying to reconstruct food webs and modes of locomotion, or they can be about looking at patterns over time, going up metre by metre in rock formations and analysing fossil groups to see how they change"

Bone secrets

Dinosaur bones are one of a palaeontologist's greatest sources of information, supplying data about their age, anatomy, distribution and much more. The bones of dinosaurs can only be found if they went through the process of fossilisation, where the tissue of the creature dissolves and gets replaced with minerals under pressure beneath the ground. Finding and extracting these fossilised bones is a major challenge for palaeontologists, with a carefully planned out dig site essential.

Discovery
Most fossils are discovered at first only in part, with just a small fragment visible above the surface

Shooting in situ
Photography plays a crucial part of any excavation. The specimen is continuously snapped from its discovery right through to removal

Clearance
Once the fossilised bone has been photographed, the rock around it is carefully cleared to allow better access to the fossils

Cleaning
When the fossil is freed from the rock, a painstaking process of cleaning follows

Tools
Clearance is achieved with chisels, hammers and spades. The closer to the fossil the more delicate the tools

Boundary
As soon as the fossil has been confirmed, a boundary is staked, protecting the area so palaeontologists can work unhindered

Extraction
The fossil is cut from the surrounding rock and removed piece by piece, with each one meticulously labelled

Packed up
The fragile specimens need to be transported with great care, with fossils placed in padded containers

Analysis
At the research lab, the fossil can be studied in depth, with laser scanning revealing in-depth detail about the dinosaur

D Diplodocus: a dino titan

Of all the dinosaurs that lived on Earth few can truly lay claim to be a terrestrial giant – but the Diplodocus can. Built like a suspension bridge, the Diplodocus measured over 25 metres (82 feet) long – that's longer than five African elephants! It weighed over 12 tons, roughly 170 times more than the average human. It had an incredibly long neck and counterweight tail, the former used to elevate its head into the foliage of trees for food, while the latter was its primary form of defence. With a typical Diplodocus estimated to have lived between 50 and 80 years, it also had one of the longest life spans of any dinosaur from the Jurassic period.

F Feathered fiends

Since palaeontologists began uncovering dinosaur remains in the 19th century, our depictions of them in the flesh have been largely coloured by a few initial artist impressions, with figures such as Charles Knight often drawing species in inaccurate postures and with factually incorrect sizes, colours and features. Based on current evidence, the lack of feathers on most species is one of the most obvious flaws in these early depictions, with half of all non-avian theropods now thought to have been partly feathered. The main cause for these misassumptions has been the lack of evidence, with feathers and soft tissues rarely preserved like fossilised bone.

"Colour in dinosaur feathers was a topic I think people thought that we would never know the answers to. But we were able to rely on a fair number of fossil feathers that were exceptionally well preserved and deep within their internal structure we could see colour-bearing organelles. So by using some smart observations and techniques we have proved it to be possible"

E Extinction

Dinosaurs perished some 65 million years ago in what is known as the K-Pg (formerly K-T) extinction event. This cataclysmic event at the Cretaceous-Palaeogene boundary led to 75 per cent of all species on Earth dying off. From the smallest ocean plankton to the largest land beasts, the K-Pg extinction event resulted in devastation at every level of the world's ecosystems, with all non-avian dinosaurs eradicated. The current theory for the catalyst of this global wipeout is an asteroid impact in South America, but the real cause for such widespread carnage was not the impact itself but its knock-on effects. These include plants not being able to photosynthesise due to dust blocking out the Sun plus a series of epic tsunamis and fire storms.

G Genetic legacy

Today the study of dinosaurs is entering an exciting new age, where we can achieve an unprecedented level of accuracy through cutting-edge analysis. After a T-rex's soft tissue was discovered within a bone sample, we can now study things like proteins, blood vessels and other micro-anatomy to help us determine how individuals lived and died, as well as how dinos evolved.

H Hunting strategies

Whether dinos hunted and scavenged alone like the T-rex or in large packs like the Deinonychus – the model for the Velociraptor in Jurassic Park – carnivorous dinosaurs were no doubt the apex predators on Earth. However, debate rages as to how co-ordinated dinosaur pack hunters were. Since first described in 1969 by palaeontologist John Ostrom, the Deinonychus has been imprinted in the public consciousness as a highly intelligent, synchronised team hunter. However, many modern dino experts disagree with this assumption, believing that while Deinonychus did move and chase prey in groups, they did so with little co-ordination, with each individual simply acting out of self-interest rather than working together like, say, lions.

Ichthyosaurus

Although technically not a true 'dinosaur', Ichthyosaurus, or 'fish lizard', filled the same niche in Earth's oceans and was one of the most dominant marine species of the Mesozoic era (252-65.5 Ma) Resembling today's dolphins, Ichthyosaurus measured in at roughly two metres (6.6 feet) in length and was capable of cruising through the water at around 40 kilometres (25 miles) per hour, enabling it to catch fish and squid with ease. The fact that Ichthyosaurus had a very large pair of eyes protected by a pair of bony, structural-supporting rings has led some palaeontologists to believe the species frequently hunted at great depths where pressure was very high.

❶ Eyes
Large eyes were protected by rings of bone to keep them intact at great depths.

❷ Teeth
The jaws were lined with rows of sharp, conical teeth, primed for shredding soft prey such as squid.

❸ Fins
Stunted limb-like fins were used for stability and manoeuvring rather than propulsion.

❹ Prey
Fish, squid and marine reptiles were the main food of Ichthyosaurus, but the sharp teeth could crush shellfish as well.

❺ Body
Its body was streamlined, with a curved spine and no neck. By undulating its body it could alter its speed and direction.

❻ Tail
A top speed of 40km/h (25mph) came courtesy of the bilobed, shark-like tail.

Jurassic lark Five factual bloopers from the famous Hollywood films

Timing problems
Jurassic Park portrayed many famous dinosaur species, including T-rex and Triceratops, but most of the animals shown actually lived in the Cretaceous period, not the Jurassic.

Out of proportion
One thing the film's producers definitely need punishing for is the depiction of the park's Velociraptors. Portrayed as being as tall as a man, in reality they barely stood 0.5m (1.6ft) off the ground.

Feather-brained
Another massive omission in Jurassic Park was the lack of any feathers. Most dinosaur species, especially sauropods, had some plumage on their bodies.

No grudge match
In the third film, the Spinosaurus is shown going toe-to-toe with its supposed arch-nemesis, the T-rex. In reality they never met as they lived on different continents of prehistoric Earth.

Spit on a grave
Another creative addition was Dilophosaurus's ability to spit out venom. However there is no evidence to suggest it could do this; neither did it have a frilled neck.

King of the dinosaurs

While not the biggest or smartest, the Tyrannosaurus rex was no doubt the closest to a king the dinosaurs ever had. A colossal bipedal carnivore, the T-rex measured in at over four metres (13 feet) tall and over 12 metres (39 feet) long, weighing over seven tons. It was no slow-poke either, with computer models estimating that the dino was capable of hitting a top speed of around 29 kilometres (18 miles) per hour chasing prey. When it caught up it could quickly dispatch them with a single bite that had a force of three tonnes – the equivalent weight of a fully grown African elephant. Yikes!

Skull
A heavy skull was adapted to withstand biting and shearing forces, with particularly strong nasal bones

Lungs
Evidence of honeycomb structures within its vertebrae suggest that T-rex breathed through a complex system of pockets and air sacs

Forelimbs
The T-rex's front limbs were short and stocky, with each exhibiting a thick cortical bone. They were used to hold on to struggling prey

Heart
With a body bigger than a bus, the T-rex needed a huge pump to transport blood at adequate pressure. Current estimates suggest its heart was over 100 times bigger than a human's

Stomach
The T-rex had a hardy stomach due to its high-meat diet and the fact that it scavenged frequently from long-dead carcasses. Analysed T-rex dung has revealed many fragments of bone

Lufeng: a fossil treasure trove

One of the most prolific dinosaur hotspots in the world is Lufeng in Yunnan Province, China. Since 1938, 33 species, each with its own complete fossil, have been found there. Some of the finds have been record-breaking, with many of the vertebrate fossils uncovered the oldest on record – the Lufengosaurus fossil (right) dates from 190 million years ago. Lufengosaurus was a genus of prosauropod that lived during the Early Jurassic period. Excavated finds can be seen at the Lufeng Dinosaur Museum.

Mesozoic world

Beginning 252.2 million years ago and coming to a close about 65 million years ago, encompassing a colossal stretch of time that includes the Triassic, Jurassic and Cretaceous periods, the Mesozoic era truly defined the age of dinosaurs. All the famous species you can think of lived within it.

The Mesozoic was generally warm with a significantly smaller temperature differential between the equatorial and polar regions – ideal conditions for the emergence and proliferation of flora and fauna. Not only was the Mesozoic famous for its domination by dinosaurs, but also for being the time period where the ancestors of today's major plant and animal groups emerged.

Oceans & continents

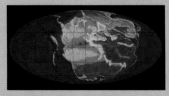

1 Triassic
At the beginning of the Mesozoic era in the Early Triassic period, all the land on Earth was joined together into the supercontinent of Pangaea, itself surrounded by the superocean Panthalassa.

Nesting & dinosaur eggs

Dinos organised their nests, laying their eggs in patterns suggesting complex social behaviours. Palaeontologists have identified two main types of egg-laying strategies – clutches and linear patterns – further divided by the shape of the nest and distribution of eggs. For example, the ornithopod Maiasaura nests generally consisted of bowl-shaped excavations roughly two metres (6.6 feet) wide and 0.8 metres (2.6 feet) deep, the opening covered by loose vegetation. Each nest was spaced roughly seven metres (22 feet) apart and was used by their offspring until they were over a metre (3.3 feet) long.

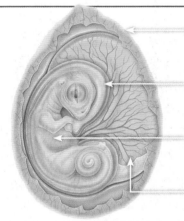

Outer shell
Dinosaur eggs were elongated and had hard, brittle shells. Some of the largest found to date were 0.6m (2ft) long

Amniotic membrane
Encompassing the dinosaur was a thin membrane, helping keep the embryo hydrated during development

Embryo
At the centre lay the dinosaur embryo that, depending on the species, could take weeks or months to hatch

Yolk sac
This contained proteins and fat which served as food for the baby dino

2 Jurassic
As the Mesozoic progressed and the Triassic made way for the Jurassic period, plate tectonics split Pangaea into two mega-continents: Gondwana and Laurasia, separated by the Tethys Sea.

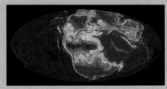

Palaeontology: key players

Most of our current knowledge of the dinosaur kingdom comes courtesy of palaeontologists, who dedicate their lives to uncovering the secrets of their prehistoric kingdom. From the earliest dinosaur hunters such as Othniel Marsh (pictured left), who discovered and named the Allosaurus, Stegosaurus and Triceratops, to 20th-century scientists who revolutionised our understanding of the dinosaurs' legacy, such as John Ostrom who gained fame for his suggestion that birds were modern-day descendants, palaeontologists have helped provide tantalising glimpses of the prehistoric world.

One of the more contemporary palaeontologists who has helped introduce dinosaurs to the general public is Dr Philip J Currie. He is also a museum curator who helped found the prestigious Royal Tyrrell Museum of Palaeontology in Alberta, Canada.

Pelvis
The T-rex was a saurischian dinosaur, meaning it had a lizard hip arrangement. Its pubis bone pointed forward and down rather than backward and down like ornithischian species

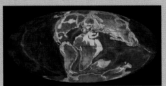

3 Cretaceous
As the Mesozoic came to a close, Gondwana and Laurasia had split into many of the continents we know today, including North and South America and Antarctica.

"Weighing something like five tons yet walking bipedally makes the T-rex incredibly interesting, as it pushes the absolute limits of what is possible. I mean, you look at an elephant and think, 'Wow, that's amazing', however, an elephant has to walk on four legs and weighs roughly the same amount, so understanding how T-rex functioned is a fascinating area of research"

Body
Unlike popular depictions, it did not stand vertical on its large hind legs but leaned forward with its body approximately parallel to the ground

Queensland

If you were to visit Queensland's more remote regions, you may very well find yourself standing face to face with one of many 100-million-year-old beasts. That's because Queensland's outback was once part of the Great Inland Sea, a huge swampy inland ocean that existed in the age of the dinosaurs. As such, hundreds of fossils have been excavated from this region and there is even an established 'Australian Dinosaur Trail' that tourists can follow.

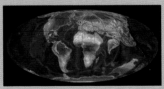

4 Palaeogene
In the Palaeogene period – immediately following the K-Pg extinction – those continents continued to move to their current positions.

Tail
A muscular tail helped counterbalance the T-rex's heavy skull and aided locomotion, improving leg retraction speeds

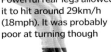

Hind legs
Powerful rear legs allowed it to hit around 29km/h (18mph). It was probably poor at turning though

Relatives in the modern world

Massive scientific effort has been put into identifying which creatures today can trace their roots back to these prehistoric beasts. One of the best examples of this was the hunt for the nearest living relative of the once-mighty T-rex, undertaken by a research team at the North Carolina State University in 2007. To go about this the researchers sequenced proteins from a 68-million-year-old T-rex tissue sample and, much to their surprise, discovered that the king of the dinosaurs' molecules showed remarkable similarity to the common chicken and that its collagen makeup was almost identical. So, at least for the time being, the humble chicken is the rightful ruler of the Earth…

Plates
Two rows of triangular back plates are believed to have acted as key components of a thermoregulatory system, serving as organic radiators

Skull
The skull was relatively small, slender and low to the ground, helping it graze on low-growing plants and vegetation

Body
Due to Stegosaurus being vegetarian, it had a large stomach perfectly adapted to breaking down tough plant matter

Tail
The powerful tail was tipped with bone spikes and could be swung at speed as a form of self-defence

S Stegosaurus
One of the most recognisable dinosaurs of all time, the Stegosaurus – despite its herbivorous nature – was a formidable opponent, with its large muscular tail tipped with lethal bone spikes. With a length of about nine metres (30 feet) and a typical weight of two to three tonnes, the Stegosaurus had a rounded body and heavy skull. Stegosaurus lived in the Late Jurassic period around 150 MYA.

Legs
The front limbs were far shorter than the hind limbs, granting its characteristically arched appearance

T Tall tails
You'll struggle to find a dinosaur without a tail. This is because the majority of dinosaurs used their tails for two important roles: the first being balance and the second being self-defence. Large animals like the T-rex and Diplodocus, thanks to their skulls or necks, were very top-heavy.

They needed long and heavy tails to counterbalance this, especially when running. Smaller creatures such as Ankylosaurus (left) used its tail when under attack, evolving a large bony club at the end which could bludgeon assailants.

U Unenlagia: half bird, half dinosaur
One of the most telling links between dinosaurs and birds is the Unenlagia, a genus of theropod dinosaur from the Late Cretaceous that in almost all aspects, aside from flight, resembles a modern bird. It was discovered in 1997 and to date two species have been confirmed – U comahuensis and U paynemili – both of which share an almost identical pelvic structure to the early bird species Archaeopteryx.

V Velociraptors debunked
Due to their appearance in the Jurassic Park films, the Velociraptor is easily one of the most recognisable of all species. Importantly though, this image of the Velociraptor is way off the mark in terms of reality.

In contrast to the movie monster, research evidence suggests that the Velociraptor was actually a feathered dinosaur under 0.6 metres (two feet) in length, with colourful plumage used in mating rituals and visual displays. The species also had hollow bones, much like birds, and built large nests to protect their offspring.

The Velociraptor did impress in ground speed, with it capable of hitting 39 kilometres (24 miles) per hour at top speed and boasting amazing agility, being able to change direction incredibly quickly. It used this speed to chase down prey, which largely consisted of small to medium-sized herbivores such as Protoceratops, and then kill them with its nine-centimetre (3.5-inch) retractable claws and sharp teeth.

New research suggests that, while sociable compared with other carnivores, raptors were not apex pack hunters, with co-operative kills possible but infrequent.

Winged wonders

While not technically dinosaurs, pterosaurs were very much the winged wonders of the dinosaur era. Flying reptiles that evolved throughout the Late Triassic and dominated the skies until the Late Cretaceous, pterosaurs were the earliest vertebrates currently known to have evolved powered flight. Pterosaurs are not related to modern-day birds or bats, with the many species evolving earlier and separately.

The genus Pterodactylus was one of the most notable, with the species Pterodactylus antiquus one of the most impressive, with a toothed beak, large eyes and clawed wings. In terms of wingspan P antiquus could extend its wings up to a metre (3.3 feet) and had a long, narrow skull packed with dozens of sharp, pointed teeth. It used these to snap up fish and smaller reptiles.

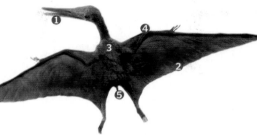

"Microraptor was a small, four-winged dinosaur... very close to the origin of birds. Its remains show it had wings on its arms and legs. It couldn't fly properly, but used its wings to glide. This shows the origin of flight in birds and their ancestors was much more complex than expected"

❶ Beak
Up to 90 teeth in the long beak intermeshed when the jaw was closed, and were perfect for grabbing fast prey.

❷ Wings
A wingspan of around 1m (3.3ft) was typical for Pterodactylus, with the wings structured in a way that indicates it would have flown like an albatross.

❸ Body
Not as large as depicted in fiction, Pterodactylus was very lightly built with hollow bones and a long neck.

❹ Limbs
Pterosaurs evolved a unique pteroid bone on the wrists of their forearms, used to support the forward wing membrane located between the wrist and shoulder.

❺ Tail
Unlike some other pterosaurs, Pterodactylus had a relatively short, stubby tail.

X-raying prehistoric remains

X-ray scanners have become incredibly useful and important tools in the world of palaeontology as they can reveal many fossils and features that otherwise would remain hidden. For example, in November 2013, researchers in Germany used an X-ray machine to unveil the detailed structure of a fossil trapped within a plaster cast, all without ever having to break it open and risking damage to the specimen. What's more, the researchers then made use of a 3D printer to re-create the X-ray scans in solid form, allowing palaeontologists to pick up and handle a cast of the fossil as fine and detailed as the real thing. Modern technology is set to further our understanding of dinosaurs by no bounds.

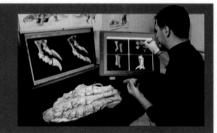

Yucatán impact

The colossal Chicxulub crater in the Yucatán Peninsula, Mexico, since its discovery in the Seventies, has heavily hinted as to how 75 per cent of all life on Earth was eradicated around 65.5 million years ago. The crater indicates that a space rock – probably an asteroid – at least ten kilometres (six miles) across impacted Earth. As a result of the extensive damage caused directly by the collision and consequently by tsunamis, dust storms and volcanism, it caused a total collapse in the world's ecosystems, with all non-avian dinosaurs at the top of the death list. Despite being challenged repeatedly, the impact's link to the K-Pg mass extinction has recently been reaffirmed with even more detail, with a research team linking the two events in time to within 11,000 years. That said, the researchers also highlighted that various precursory phenomena, such as dramatic climate swings, also contributed to the end of the dinosaurs post-impact.

Zalmoxes sized up

Zalmoxes, a genus of herbivorous dinosaur from the Late Cretaceous period, is believed by some to be one of the earliest examples of insular dwarfism – a condition whereby a species undergoes a continuous reduction in size to better suit its environment, shrinking over several generations. Fossils from at least two species of Zalmoxes have been found in central Europe and one of its closest ancestors is thought to be the much larger Iguanodon.

What was a dinosaur?

Dinosaurs were a reptile that first appeared over 230 million years ago. They lived on Earth longer than any other creature in history

Dinosaurs dominated the Earth for over 160 million years, often as the apex predators of their particular environments. Although fossilised dinosaur remains have been discovered throughout human history (early discoveries probably being the origins of mythical creatures such as dragons and hydras), dinosaurs were only described scientifically in the early nineteenth century. It was British palaeontologist Sir Richard Owen who coined the taxon Dinosauria in 1842. The word dinosaur means "terrible lizard", but the term is somewhat misleading, as dinosaurs are not lizards but are part of a separate group of reptiles altogether. Dinosaurs are a diverse group that began life on the super-continent of Pangaea. As continental shift progressed and Pangaea broke up into smaller landmasses, dinosaurs became strongly diversified. It's a wonder that Triceratops and T-rex share a common ancestor.

Defence
Thick skin and hard armour shells made these dinosaurs tough as nails

Four-legged dinosaurs

Most plant-eating dinosaurs had hip bones similar to the birds of today. They walked on four legs and evolved to protect themselves against predators. Some had huge horns for defence.

Protection
Massive horns were ideal to protect against predators

Two-legged dinosaurs

Most meat-eating dinosaurs had hip bones like the lizards of today and moved around on two legs. This gave them the ability to run very fast to catch prey. Strangely, today's birds evolved from lizard-hipped dinosaurs.

Plesiosaurs

Some plesiosaurs had long, flexible necks. They used these to catch nimble fish

"Dinosaurs are a diverse group of reptiles, beginning life on the super-continent of Pangaea"

Attack
By running on two feet, predatory dinosaurs could reach high speeds

NOT ACTUALLY DINOSAURS

Swimming reptiles

The oceans of the world were once ruled by ichthyosaurs, plesiosaurs and mosasaurs, not dinosaurs. Many of these underwater animals looked a lot like modern-day fish. They were perfectly adapted for life in the sea and fossils show that they may have given birth to live young.

Pterosaurs
Many pterosaur fossils show they had incredibly strong muscles, perfect for flying

Pterosaurs

Though they were around at the same time, most flying creatures in this period were not actually dinosaurs. These winged reptiles ruled the skies with their big brains and deadly beaks.

When did dinosaurs rule the Earth?

Dinosaurs roamed Earth between 230 and 65 million years ago, when our planet was very different to today

Jurassic period
200 to 145 million years ago
The Jurassic period is called the 'Age of the Reptiles' because it was during this time that reptiles ruled the planet

Diplodocus

Augustasaurus

Pliosaurus

The first dinosaurs
Staurikosaurus is one of the very first dinosaurs

Continents
Around the world, land moved to make more coastlines

Flora
Lush jungles covered much of the land

Permian period
300 to 250 million years ago
It was extremely hot during this time. While there were oceans, the land was very much like a desert. Only reptiles would be able to thrive in this environment

Triassic period
250 to 200 million years ago
It might have been quite hot and dry, but that didn't stop the very first mammals and flying reptiles from appearing. Trees and plants also grew in the places we know today as the cold and icy south and north poles

Chasmatosaurus

Triassic fish and ocean reptiles lived in the warm seas

Edaphosaurus

Ichthyosaurs

Ivantosaurus

Lystrosaurus

Cynognathus

The first true mammals began to evolve during the Triassic period

High temperatures
It might have been very hot, but some places had rain

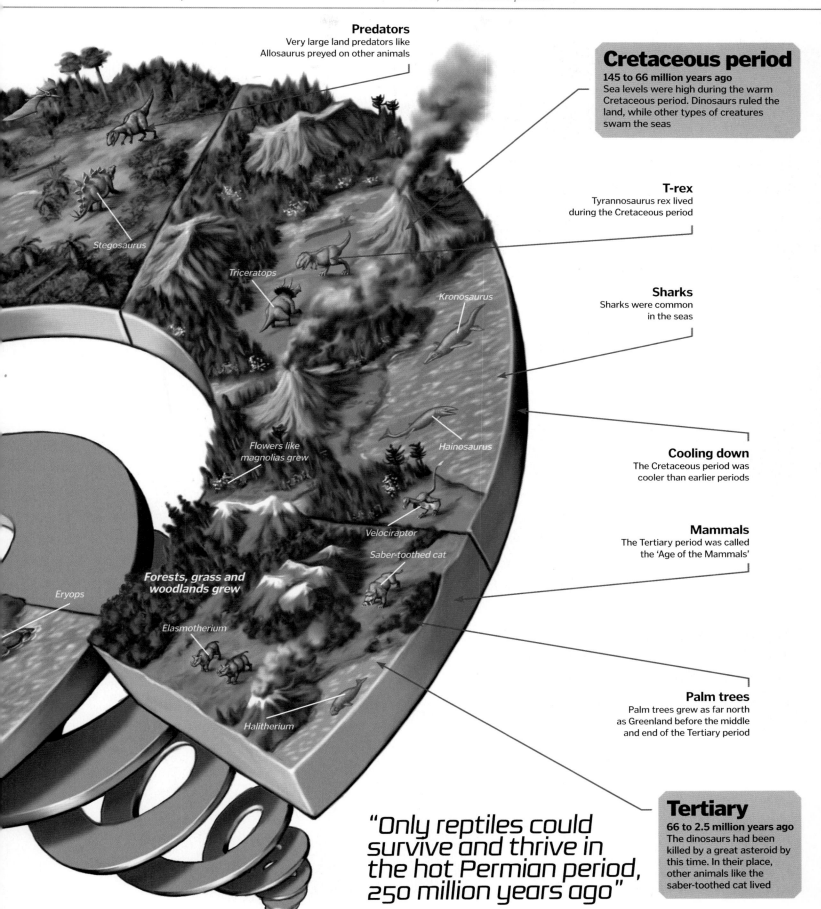

Predators
Very large land predators like
Allosaurus preyed on other animals

Stegosaurus

Triceratops

Kronosaurus

Hainosaurus

*Flowers like
magnolias grew*

Velociraptor

Saber-toothed cat

**Forests, grass and
woodlands grew**

Eryops

Elasmotherium

Halitherium

Cretaceous period
145 to 66 million years ago
Sea levels were high during the warm
Cretaceous period. Dinosaurs ruled the
land, while other types of creatures
swam the seas

T-rex
Tyrannosaurus rex lived
during the Cretaceous period

Sharks
Sharks were common
in the seas

Cooling down
The Cretaceous period was
cooler than earlier periods

Mammals
The Tertiary period was called
the 'Age of the Mammals'

Palm trees
Palm trees grew as far north
as Greenland before the middle
and end of the Tertiary period

Tertiary
66 to 2.5 million years ago
The dinosaurs had been
killed by a great asteroid by
this time. In their place,
other animals like the
saber-toothed cat lived

*"Only reptiles could
survive and thrive in
the hot Permian period,
250 million years ago"*

Where did dinosaurs live?

Dinosaurs lived all over the world, from dry, dusty deserts to wet, sweaty swamps. Explore five different habitats that dinosaurs called home...

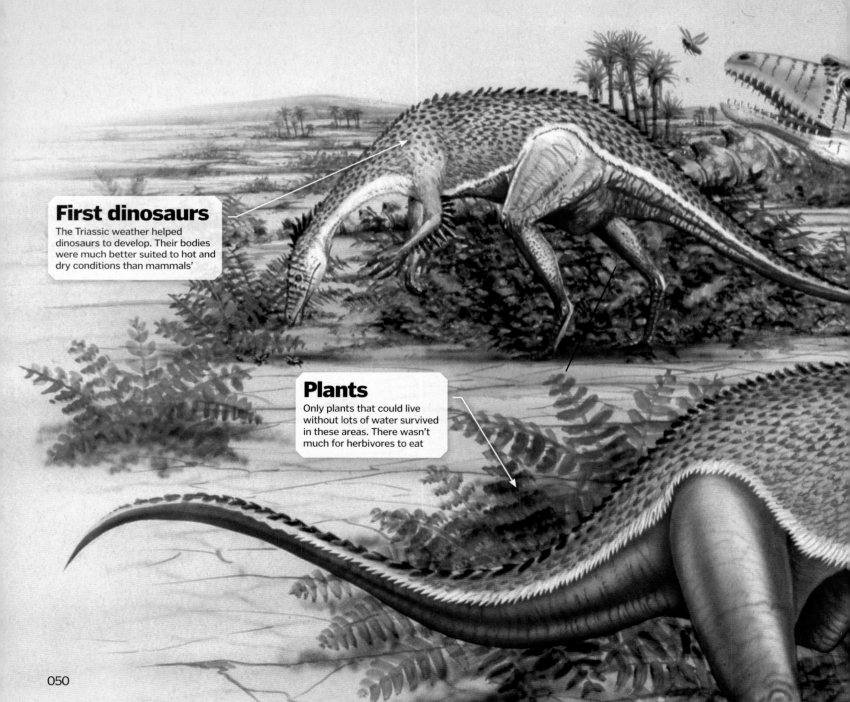

First dinosaurs

The Triassic weather helped dinosaurs to develop. Their bodies were much better suited to hot and dry conditions than mammals'

Plants

Only plants that could live without lots of water survived in these areas. There wasn't much for herbivores to eat

Triassic desert

250 to 200 million years ago

Dinosaurs first appeared during the Triassic period. Earth was hot, dry and covered in deserts

Extinction

Before the Triassic period began, almost all life had died out. Earth was recovering from the biggest extinction event ever

Passing through

Dinosaurs only travelled deep into the desert for food. Some areas were too hot to live in all the time

Coelophysis

Dinosaurs like Coelophysis hunted in these areas

Dinosaur habitat

Triassic forest
250 to 200 million years ago
The weather was milder at the north and south poles.
It was drier so large forests grew

Trees
Most trees in these forests were tall with tough leaves. They were evergreens so didn't lose their leaves over winter

No ice caps
Even the north and south poles were warm. They weren't icy and frozen like Antarctica and the Arctic are today

Fresh water
Rivers provided fresh water to drink

Food
Some Triassic herbivores stood on two legs and had long necks. This let them reach higher leaves on tall trees

No grass
There was no grass during the Triassic period. The ground was covered in small plants like ferns and mosses instead

Early mammals
The first mammals started to evolve

Jurassic swamp
200 to 145 million years ago
Sea levels were higher during the Jurassic period.
Some land got flooded, which created muddy swamps

Bigger dinosaurs
Herbivores got bigger because there were
more plants for them to eat. Carnivores
also grew as their prey got larger

Plants
Trees spread across Jurassic
Earth. They started growing
in places that were too dry
for them back in the Triassic

Tree life
Small animals lived
in the trees

Weather

Regular rainy seasons kept the soil damp. This watered ferns and other small ground plants that herbivores could consume

Continents moving

As Pangaea split up, the new continents had different habitats like swamps. Animals evolved quickly to survive in these new areas

Jurassic ocean

200 to 145 million years ago

Reptiles didn't just live on land. Massive prehistoric monsters ruled the Jurassic oceans as well

Oceanic predators
Plesiosaurs and Ichthyosaurs were top predators

Plenty of food
Smaller creatures like fish and molluscs were everywhere. They made easy meals for bigger beasts like reptiles, sharks and whales

New oceans

The continents split apart and drifted away from each other. Oceans flooded the spaces in between to make new seas

Ocean giants

Marine reptiles grew to incredible sizes in Jurassic oceans. Plesiosaurs and ocean crocodiles reached the same sizes as modern whales

Floor food

Dead creatures sank to the bottom of the sea. Their bodies were eaten by animals living on the ocean floor

Cretaceous plains

145 to 66 million years ago
Life was not easy on the Cretaceous plains. Dinosaurs faced many changes to their habitat

Wildfires
During the Cretaceous period, lightning struck trees and started fires. Because there were plenty of plants, flames could spread quickly

Herds
Some dinosaurs survived better in groups

Flowers
Lots of different flowering plants evolved. Their pollen was spread by insects like bees. Flowers eventually outnumbered trees and shrubs

Atmosphere

There were a lot of active volcanoes at this time. They filled the air with carbon dioxide and other gases

Climate

Continents drifted further apart. This made the ocean currents change. Currents affected the weather, making temperatures go up and down

The dinosaurs' neighbours

Tiny mammals lived alongside dinosaurs in the Mesozoic era. While many are now extinct, some of their ancestors are still alive today

Mammals evolved during the Triassic period, about the same time as the first dinosaurs appeared. Their reptilian contemporaries, the archosaurs, were the more successful creatures at the time, probably because they were better adapted to surviving the arid Triassic weather.

Early mammals are synapsids, meaning that they have an extra opening in the skull behind the eyes. This allowed strong jaws to develop.

While dinosaurs reigned, mammals never grew larger than a cat, but hardy mammals were able to grow and successfully occupy empty niches once the dinosaurs died out.

Duck-billed platypus

Cretaceous, around 120 million years ago to present
The platypus is one of the most unique mammals in the world. It lays eggs instead of giving birth and the males have venomous spurs

Palaeoryctidae

Mid-Cretaceous to early Paleogene, around 105 to 66 million years ago
These creatures looked a lot like modern-day shrews. They mainly lived in what would become North America and were very small

Multituberculata

Late Jurassic to early Oligocene, 160 to 35 million years ago
This group of little mammals was around for roughly 120 million years. It's the longest-surviving mammal group on record

"Mammals were able to successfully occupy empty niches once the dinosaurs died out"

Cynognathus

Triassic, around 230 million years ago
These creatures were also technically mammal-like lizards. They had many features in common with mammals, such as hair and possibly even warm blood

HOW IT WORKS

BOOK OF DINOSAURS

DINOSAURS

076
Triceratops

© Eva Kröcher

096 Quetzalcoatlus

© DK Images

090
Marine reptiles

© SPL

103
Giganotosaurus

© Alamy

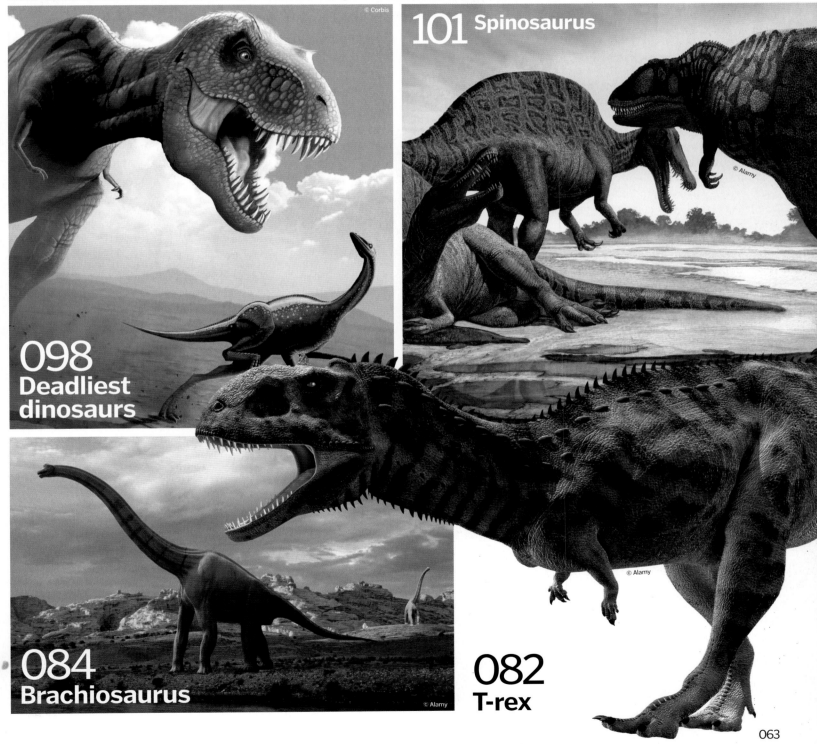

074
Diplodocus

079
Velociraptor claws

© SPL

© Corbis

101 Spinosaurus

© Alamy

098
Deadliest dinosaurs

084
Brachiosaurus

© Alamy

082
T-rex

© Alamy

What's inside a dinosaur egg?

Just like modern day baby chicks, dinosaurs grew and hatched from eggs to roam the planet a very long time ago

What came first – the dinosaur or the egg? We're not entirely sure, but what we do know is that these great reptiles laid eggs just like chickens do. Inside the shell of a hen's egg, chicks are able to grow before they're ready to hatch. That's just how the dinosaurs were born.

We know that baby dinosaurs were made this way because we have found lots of evidence. Fossilised dinosaur eggs have been found at over 200 places across the world. They tell a story about how the dinosaur made its nest, laid its eggs and how baby dinosaurs were born.

A crew of palaeontologists exploring Mongolia in 1923 were the first to scientifically recognise fossilised dinosaur eggs for what they were. Since then many dinosaur nesting sites for many different species have been uncovered all around the world. The oldest known dinosaur eggs and embryos date back to the Early Jurassic (about 190 million years ago) and come from the Massospondylus, a bipedal, omnivorous prosauropod.

Egg Mountain in Montana, USA is the site of one of the most famous dinosaur nest discoveries. Maiasaura remains were found near a nest with the remains of eggshells and babies too large to be hatchlings and this is the reason why Maiasaura is known as "caring mother lizard". Maiasaura and many other species of dinosaur, raised their young in nest colonies. This relfected the way that they herded when on the move. This amazing discovery was the first proof that dinosaurs raised and fed their young, rather than leaving hatchlings to fend for themselves like modern turtles do. Nests contained approximately 30-40 eggs and were not incubated by the parent sitting on them, but by the heat produced from rotting vegetation placed in the nest. It's thought that Maiasaura hatchlings left the nest after a year or two of rapid growth.

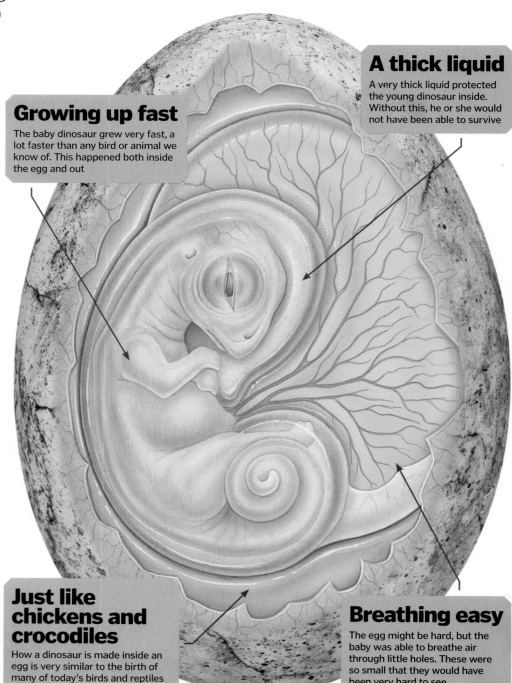

A thick liquid
A very thick liquid protected the young dinosaur inside. Without this, he or she would not have been able to survive

Growing up fast
The baby dinosaur grew very fast, a lot faster than any bird or animal we know of. This happened both inside the egg and out

Just like chickens and crocodiles
How a dinosaur is made inside an egg is very similar to the birth of many of today's birds and reptiles

Breathing easy
The egg might be hard, but the baby was able to breathe air through little holes. These were so small that they would have been very hard to see

Dinosaur egg versus chicken egg

The Hypselosaurus egg is five times larger than a chicken egg

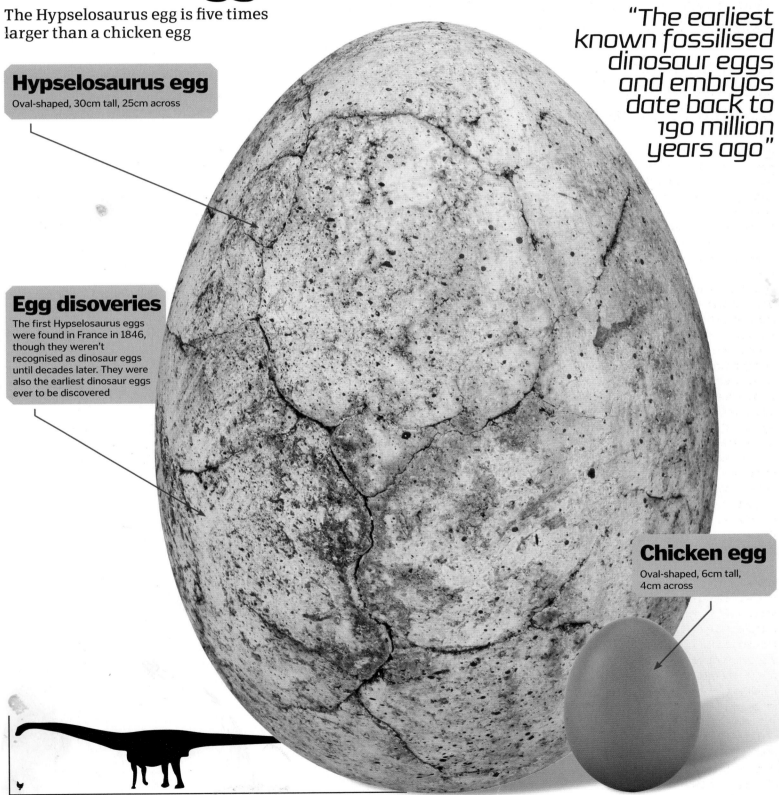

Hypselosaurus egg
Oval-shaped, 30cm tall, 25cm across

Egg disoveries
The first Hypselosaurus eggs were found in France in 1846, though they weren't recognised as dinosaur eggs until decades later. They were also the earliest dinosaur eggs ever to be discovered

"The earliest known fossilised dinosaur eggs and embryos date back to 190 million years ago"

Chicken egg
Oval-shaped, 6cm tall, 4cm across

World's biggest dinosaurs

With fossil brush in hand, we unearth the massive behemoths that ruled over land, air and sea millions of years ago

Stegosaurus
Stegosaurus was slightly larger than a shipping container, but its brain was only the size of a walnut

Brachiosaurus
The brachiosaurus used its staggering 16m (52.5 feet) height to reach tall vegetation

Flexible
Despite all this support holding the sauropod together, the design still allowed the creatures to remain surprisingly flexible

Standing
The placement of the tendon in the vertebrae allowed sauropods to hold their necks and tails upright with minimal effort

© Science Photo Library

Pterosaur

The hollow bones of a pterosaur ensured it remained light enough to achieve flight, even when reaching the size of a small plane

It's somewhat frightening to imagine what it must have been like to wander around the plains of Africa and Argentina 100 million years ago. Whereas today you'd be hard-pressed to encounter a beast any bigger than yourself, back then you'd be running for your life as bus-sized creatures roamed free, some remaining largely peaceful and distant, others full of aggression.

The biggest land-based animal alive today is the African bush elephant, with the largest weighing a measly 13.5 tons and measuring 10.6m (34.8ft) long and 4.2m (13.8ft) high. Argentinosaurus, the current official record-holder for largest dinosaur of them all, would have been at least four times the size. It was a sauropod, dinosaurs of the Jurassic and Cretaceous period that were mostly herbivores and known for being very large. Indeed, many other types of sauropod would have stood tall above the African bush elephant, as would raptors and pterosaurs.

Dinosaurs inhabited the Earth for much longer than any modern animal, from 251 to 65 million years ago, allowing plenty of time for certain species to develop into the giant hulks of flesh we now so revere. The biggest dinosaurs discovered to date have largely been determined to live in the Late Cretaceous period, 99.6-65.5 million years ago, before they faced extinction.

For a long time, though, palaeontologists have wondered why dinosaurs grew to be so large. While impressive, size can also be a hindrance. Not only does a large animal need a much higher rate of metabolism, but it must also develop much stronger bones and skeletal structures to be able to hold itself upright. Many of these gigantic animals were also cumbersome and slow, leaving themselves open to attack from large predators. Why did dinosaurs continue to grow for millions of years, then?

One train of thought is that there was a huge surplus of carbon dioxide in the atmosphere during the age of the dinosaurs. This meant that vegetation flourished, and herbivores such as the sauropods simply had an over-abundance of nourishment available to eat. While somewhat of a burden in terms of manoeuvrability, their size would certainly have helped to some extent when fending off smaller carnivores. This leads to another proposal from palaeontologists, namely that some dinosaurs grew in size over millions of years as a form of self-defence.

However, others think that these giant dinosaurs were cold-blooded, which was directly responsible for their size. Indeed, warm-blooded animals simply wouldn't be able to sustain such mammoth sizes, somewhat backed up by the lack of mammals larger than a few tons today.

Huge cold-blooded sauropods, weighing in at up to 100 tons, would have been almost self-sustainable, as they could store heat throughout the day for the colder nights, maintaining a fairly unchanged body temperature and prolonging their survival.

How were they supported?

We examine the anatomy of a sauropod, to see how these huge creatures were able to keep upright

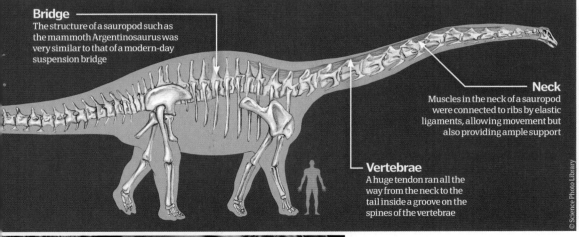

Bridge
The structure of a sauropod such as the mammoth Argentinosaurus was very similar to that of a modern-day suspension bridge

Neck
Muscles in the neck of a sauropod were connected to ribs by elastic ligaments, allowing movement but also providing ample support

Vertebrae
A huge tendon ran all the way from the neck to the tail inside a groove on the spines of the vertebrae

© Science Photo Library

© Science Photo Library

BIGGEST OVERALL

Argentinosaurus

Argentinosaurus is the largest-known dinosaur to have ever lived, based on fossilised evidence. Weighing in at over 100 tons and measuring as much as 45 metres (148 feet) in length, this herbivore was wider and longer than a basketball court and was as heavy as a fuel-less jumbo jet.

The vertebrae of the Argentinosaurus were very broad, with small peg-and-socket articulations above the spinal cord that kept the backbones of these animals sturdy and rigid. In addition, the ribs of the Argentinosaurus were hollow, possibly allowing for greater manoeuvrability. Although the skull, neck and tail of an Argentinonsaurus have never been found, measurements made from a shinbone can estimate the size of the various features of this colossal creature. Each hind limb of the Argentinosaurus would have been about 4.5 metres (15 feet) long.

The statistics...

Argentinosaurus

Weight: >100 tonnes

Length: <45m (148ft)

Height: 21m (70ft)

Date: Late Cretaceous (99.6-65.6 Ma)

Group: Sauropodomorphs

Bigger than: A basketball court

Tail
The spinosaur's tail was incredibly strong, with huge muscles at its base allowing it to be potentially used as a weapon

BIGGEST CARNIVORE

Spinosaurus

The Spinosaurus is often overlooked as the largest carnivorous dinosaur in favour of its more famous cousin, the Tyrannosaurus rex. However, the Spinosaurus would have dwarfed the popular movie star, measuring 16m (52ft) in length compared to 12m (39ft) for a T-rex. That being said, the characteristic features of the Spinosaurus – namely its fin-like spinal protrusion – make it one of the most recognisable theropods. In the late-Cretaceous period, this 12-tonne creature would have been fairly common, with its sail-like spine adding to a fearsome display and possibly helping to regulate its body temperature.

Sail
Tall bony spines growing upwards from the vertebrae of the Spinosaur supported its characteristic sail-like structure

Teeth
Within its crocodile-like snout, an unusual feature for a theropod, were rows of conical teeth for hunting and killing fish and average-sized land-based dinosaurs

Feet
At the base of the strong hind legs of the Spinosaur were three long, forward-facing claws

The statistics...

Spinosaurus

Weight: 12 tonnes

Length: 16m (52ft)

Date: Late Cretaceous (99.6-65.6 Ma)

Group: Theropods

Bigger than: A double-decker bus

The other contenders

There is some contention among paleontologists as to what the largest dinosaur of all time was. Currently the official record-holder is the 100-tonne behemoth that is Argentinosaurus. However, there have been several other claims to the throne over the years. In the late-19th Century, a paleontologist known as Edward Cope claimed to have found part of a vertebra that suggested he had unearthed a sauropod dinosaur (known as 'amphicoelias') measuring a humongous 62m (203ft). Mysteriously, however, this bone 'disappeared' shortly afterwards, leading some to believe he had falsified the claim to get one over on his chief paleontological rival at the time, Othniel Marsh. It will be interesting to see if any more evidence of this giant creature is unearthed in future. Another contender that little is known about is Bruhathkayosaurus, which may possibly be the heaviest dinosaur ever discovered, coming in at up to a gigantic 220 tonnes.

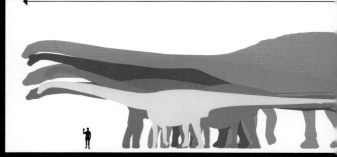

The statistics...

Quetzalcoatlus

Weight: <250kg

Wingspan: 12m (39ft)

Date:
Late Cretaceous (99.6-65.6 Ma)

Group: Pterosaurs

Bigger than: A small plane

BIGGEST PTEROSAUR

Quetzalcoatlus

Although not technically regarded as 'dinosaurs', pterosaurs were around at a similar time and are often (somewhat incorrectly) referred to as 'flying dinosaurs', much to the ire of some palaeontologists. Nevertheless they were impressive creatures, and none more so than Quetzalcoatlus, the largest flying animal of all time. Its huge 2.5m (8ft) skull housed an elongated mouth that was used to hunt land animals including dinosaurs and other vertebrates. Despite its size Quetzalcoatlus was comparatively light as its bones were comprised of a series of air sacs, a useful feature for such a colossal creature aiming to take to the skies. While most other pterosaurs fed on fish, Quetzalcoatlus was somewhat unique in its hunting of land animals, no doubt useful nutrition to fuel its giant metabolic needs.

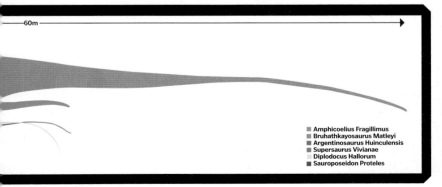

60m

■ Amphicoelius Fragillimus
■ Bruhathkayosaurus Matleyi
■ Argentinosaurus Huinculensis
■ Supersaurus Vivianae
□ Diplodocus Hallorum
■ Sauroposeidon Proteles

Dinosaur identification

We spoke to Mike Benton, Professor of Vertebrate Palaeontology in the School of Earth Science at the University of Bristol, UK, to find out how palaeontologists can estimate the size of a dinosaur from fossils and more

How It Works: Can you describe your current role within the world of palaeontology?
Mike Benton: I work in a 50:50 teaching and research position – I teach undergraduates, both geologists and keen palaeontologists, and especially I teach Masters and PhD students. Every year, some 20-25 new Masters students and four-five new PhD students come from all parts of the world to work with us, and I really enjoy working with them to help them develop their careers. In research, I work on several topics by myself, on others with my students, and on others with collaborators around the world.

Could you briefly summarise the key methods and techniques used in the identification of prehistoric creatures?
Palaeontologists identify fossils based on the existing knowledge of living and extinct forms. The fossils are often incomplete, and usually show only the hard parts, such as shells and bones. But, if there is a living relative, these parts can be identified, and a fair attempt made to identify what the fossil is. Usually, palaeontologists have many fossils of the same animal or plant to work with, and they can compare these.

Can you describe some of the challenges involved in identifying a dinosaur?
Dinosaurs are all extinct, and their closest living relatives, the birds, are so different that it is hard to make useful comparisons in many cases. But, when complete skeletons are known, all the bones can be identified from knowledge of living forms, and the skeleton can be reconstructed. This usually shows basic things, such as whether the animal walked on all fours or on its hind limbs only, what it ate (are the teeth sharp or not?), and

whether it could have used its hands for grasping things.

How are paleontologists able to discern how large a dinosaur is, and how can they estimate a dinosaur's diet?
The dinosaur skeleton will itself be large or small. The best guide to body weight for a fossil form is to measure the leg bones. The femur (thigh bone) is particularly useful – because weight (= mass) is a three-dimensional measure, we look for something that increases and decreases in proportion to mass, and that is the diameter of the femur. So you get a good relationship between femur head diameter and body mass from living birds, crocodiles and mammals, and dinosaur body weights can then be estimated from this regular relationship. Diet is determined from overall tooth shape – curved and pointy for meat-eating, and broader for plant-eating. It's hard to be more precise, because we don't have the data set of comparative information to tell exact plant food from wear marks and scratches on the tooth enamel (used for determining the exact diet of mammals).

What, in your opinion, are the most important discoveries made in the past 50 years?
Well, first, the realisation that dinosaurs were active and dynamic animals, dating from the work of John Ostrom in 1969 on Deinonychus, and Bob Bakker in the Seventies on dinosaur warm-bloodedness. Second, the paper by Luis Alvarez and colleagues in 1980 that showed the first evidence that the Earth had been hit by an asteroid 65 million years ago. This has been much confirmed since then, and even the crater has been identified, all showing the key role of this in causing the extinction of the dinosaurs.

069

How did dinosaurs defend themselves?

Dinosaurs evolved spikes, horns and even thick armoured skin to protect themselves. They needed to be able to fight off predators or risk getting eaten

Herbivorous dinosaurs developed built-in weapons to defend against carnivores. This gave them a better chance of surviving a fight against predators. It also gave them a better chance at defending vulnerable young against predation. Some dinosaurs had sharp claws on their hands, like Iguanodons, which could have been used as a tool and as a weapon. Dinosaurs like Triceratops had horns as long as a human arm that pointed forwards so that the Triceratops could take on its enemy head on. Both these defences could have been used to stab attacking predators.

Other dinosaurs used their tails as weapons. The Ankylosaurus had a heavy, bony hammer at the end of its tail. They could use this to smash into an attacking dinosaur and they were strong enough to crush skulls and break bones. Some dinosaurs were covered in tough scales like a thick coat of armour. Stegosaurus had a row of bony plates running along its spine that are thought to be used for temperature control, though it's certainly possible that they were also used for defence. The bony plates ended along the tail but Stegosaurus remained well defended by the sharp spikes at the end of its tail. Powerful muscles could propel those spikes into an oncoming attacker. Indeed, Allosaurus remains have been found with wounds that line up perfectly with the dimensions of a Stegosaurus's tail spikes

Larger herbivores used their size as a defence. Dinosaurs like the Diplodocus were so massive that carnivores couldn't attack them easily. For smaller dinosaurs, running away was usually the best defence. They developed lighter bones so they could run faster. They needed to escape quickly to avoid fighting altogether.

Frill horns
The large part of the top of their skulls is called a frill. This Styracosaurus had lots of sharp horns along the top of its frill

Tail spikes
Tail spikes could be used as weapons because they were hard and sharp. They also made dinosaurs much harder to eat.

Whip
Dinosaurs like Diplodocus had long tails that they could use like whips. It's possible that they snapped faster than the speed of sound.

Tail club
Tail clubs were swung around just like a hammer. They were smashed into predators' legs and could crush bones.

Armour plating

The Scolosaurus had a body built for defence - from a bony club at the end of its tail to thick scales covering its body

"Triceratops had pointed horns on its face as long as a human arm"

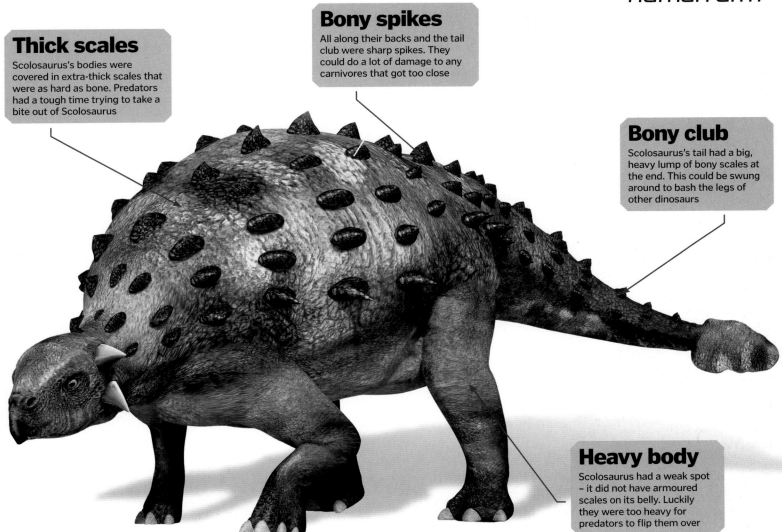

Thick scales
Scolosaurus's bodies were covered in extra-thick scales that were as hard as bone. Predators had a tough time trying to take a bite out of Scolosaurus

Bony spikes
All along their backs and the tail club were sharp spikes. They could do a lot of damage to any carnivores that got too close

Bony club
Scolosaurus's tail had a big, heavy lump of bony scales at the end. This could be swung around to bash the legs of other dinosaurs

Heavy body
Scolosaurus had a weak spot – it did not have armoured scales on its belly. Luckily they were too heavy for predators to flip them over

Horns
Horned dinosaurs might have charged towards predators to try and scare them away. Their horns could have ripped through skin.

Crest
Head crests were used for communication. Dinosaurs could make warning calls to each other if they saw a predator nearby.

Headbutt
Some dinosaurs, like Stegoceras, could smash skulls with predators. Their heads were protected by extra layers of bone for shock-absorption.

What was the cleverest dinosaur?

The Troodon was about the same size as a human, but their brain was much bigger than the other dinosaurs'. This made them very dangerous hunters

Dinosaurs were not a brainy bunch, but the Troodon was unusually smart. Its brain was much larger than other dinosaurs and it was ferocious predator. They were clever enough to hunt in packs so they could catch much larger prey. There was no escape from a Troodon.

The bird-like dinosaur was very good at running, with its long legs and curved claws that would deliver the killer blow to prey. It is thought that a Troodon's teeth were as sharp as knives and that their big eyes gave them great night vision, so they weren't limited to hunting in daylight.

Thumbs up

Troodons were the most human of all the dinosaurs. They had opposable thumbs and they could walk upright on two legs

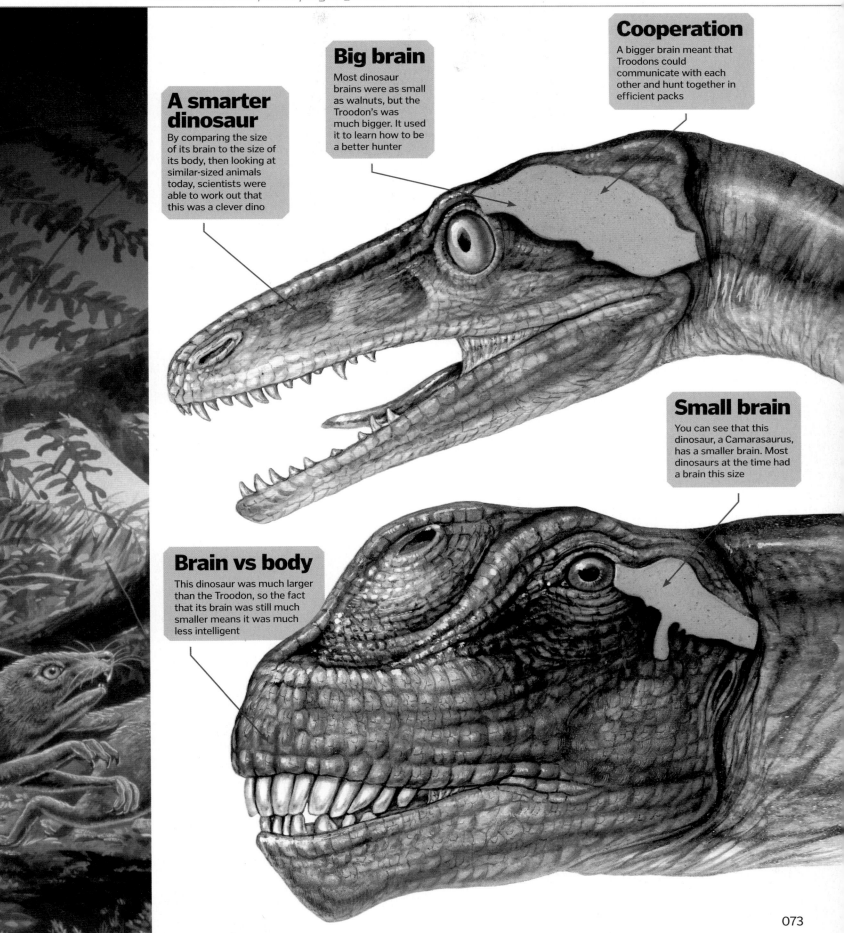

Cooperation

A bigger brain meant that Troodons could communicate with each other and hunt together in efficient packs

Big brain

Most dinosaur brains were as small as walnuts, but the Troodon's was much bigger. It used it to learn how to be a better hunter

A smarter dinosaur

By comparing the size of its brain to the size of its body, then looking at similar-sized animals today, scientists were able to work out that this was a clever dino

Small brain

You can see that this dinosaur, a Camarasaurus, has a smaller brain. Most dinosaurs at the time had a brain this size

Brain vs body

This dinosaur was much larger than the Troodon, so the fact that its brain was still much smaller means it was much less intelligent

Diplodocus

We find out how this mighty dinosaur once lived

Diplodocus is one of the most famous dinosaurs. It belonged to the group known as the sauropodomorphs and was around in the Late Jurassic period – specifically the Kimmeridgian and Tithonian eras roughly 154-150 million years ago. It reached sizes of up to 25 metres (82 feet) in length and was found in what is now North America. There were four species of Diplodocus, with the largest of these being Seismosaurus, which translates to 'ground shaker'.

Diplodocus was part of the diplodocid family, sharing the same characteristic of having 15 neck vertebrae, short forelimbs compared to the rest of its body and a whip-like tail. Its giant neck made up a large proportion of its body, but there is still some contention as to whether it held its neck vertically or horizontally. Its rectangular skull contained huge eye sockets and nasal chambers. Studies of its teeth suggest that Diplodocus fed using what is known as branch stripping, where the branch of a tree is grasped in a creature's jaw and then pulled sharply up or down, tearing off foliage.

Diplodocus was the largest dinosaur around. It was later eclipsed by other sauropods, but it roamed the tallest for at least a few million years. Numerous bones have been found and studied by palaeontologists, providing an insight into how these giant dinosaurs were able to support themselves and how they lived.

Spine
Running along its back, like other sauropods, were triangular spines on its vertebrae

Vertebrae
There were as many as 80 caudal vertebrae in the tail of the Diplodocus

Tail
It's highly likely that it was able to crack its whip-like tail at supersonic speeds, using it as a primary form of attack or defence

Diplodocus feet are believed to have been fleshy and cushioned by thick pads, much like those of elephants

© Beatrice Mlach

074

Head

Compared to the rest of its body, the Diplodocus had a very small head

Teeth

The teeth of Diplodocus were peg-like, allowing it to strip foliage from branches

Stability

The outstretched tail counterbalanced the neck of the Diplodocus, allowing the huge creature to remain stable

"Its giant neck made up a large proportion of its body, but there is still some contention as to whether it held its neck vertically or horizontally"

4m (13ft)

1.8m (5.9ft)

25m (82ft)

Legs

Diplodocus could weigh up to 15 tonnes. It therefore needed huge, trunk-like legs to support its immense body weight

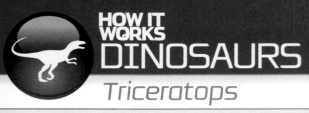

Artwork depicting Triceratops horridus, one of the last species of ceratopsia to evolve before the extinction of the dinosaurs around 65 million years ago

Frill
The Triceratops' large, solid bone frill is thought to have evolved as a courtship display aid, rather than a defensive shield structure

Tail
The long tail of the triceratops helped it to balance and counteracted the weight of its super-heavy front end

Triceratops

One of the most well-known dinosaurs, the Triceratops was a herbivorous titan that was very well equipped for a fight

Triceratops is a genus of herbivorous dinosaur that comprises two validated species – Triceratops horridus and Triceratops prorsus, both of which roamed Earth during the Late Cretaceous period (68-65 Ma) before being eradicated in the K-T mass-extinction event that wiped out all dinosaurs.

Triceratops were large, rhinoceros-like animals that weighed many tonnes – a fully grown adult would be expected to weigh in the region of seven tonnes. They were heavily armoured with reinforced bone horns, which could exceed 70 centimetres (28 inches) and a solid bone frill, and hugely powerful thanks to their sturdy frame. These traits, combined, made both species of Triceratops a fearsome foe to potential predators, capable of puncturing flesh and shattering bone with their sharp horns when charging.

In terms of anatomy (for a comprehensive rundown, see the 'Triceratops anatomy' illustration), the Triceratops genus is incredibly interesting, not least because many of its parts' functions are still debated today in the field of palaeontology. A good example of this can be seen by analysing a typical Triceratops skull, which – aside from typically measuring a whopping two metres (6.6 feet) in length – sported three horns as well as a fluted, extravagant rear frill.

The horns, from which the genus gets its name, and frill have been successfully argued by palaeontologists to have been used for self-defence against predators, with close examination of unearthed specimens revealing battle scars, cuts, punctures and cracks. However, modern scholars also postulate that both skull features, along with the elongated nature of the skull itself, most likely

also evolved as courtship aids, with potential mates selected on the size and shape of these features. It has also been suggested that the frill may have helped Triceratops regulate their body temperature in a similar manner to the plate-laden Stegosaurus (whose name translates as roof, or covered, lizard).

Other anatomical areas of interest lie in this dinosaur's large bird-like beak and hips. Indeed, it is because of these particular features that this genus has been used as a reference point in the definition of all dinosaurs – ie all dinosaurs are descendants of the most recent common ancestor of Triceratops and, as such, this common ancestor is also that of birds prevalent throughout the world today. It's important to note here that modern birds did not descend from triceratops directly, but rather from its common ancestor with all other dinosaurs; today's birds in fact originate from saurischian dinosaurs.

Triceratops anatomy

We examine the skeleton of this powerful plant-eater to see its basic anatomy

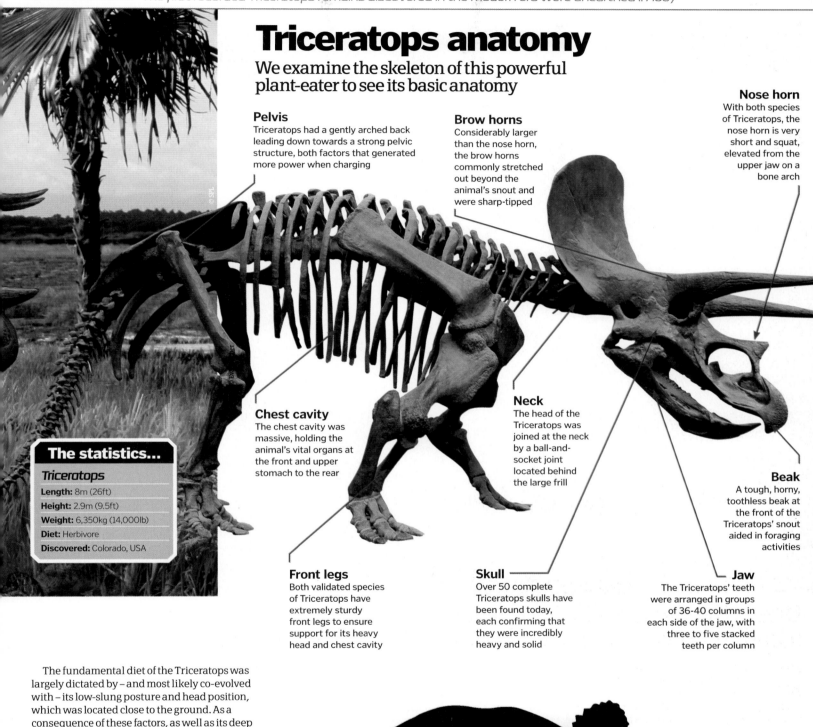

Pelvis
Triceratops had a gently arched back leading down towards a strong pelvic structure, both factors that generated more power when charging

Brow horns
Considerably larger than the nose horn, the brow horns commonly stretched out beyond the animal's snout and were sharp-tipped

Nose horn
With both species of Triceratops, the nose horn is very short and squat, elevated from the upper jaw on a bone arch

Chest cavity
The chest cavity was massive, holding the animal's vital organs at the front and upper stomach to the rear

Neck
The head of the Triceratops was joined at the neck by a ball-and-socket joint located behind the large frill

Beak
A tough, horny, toothless beak at the front of the Triceratops' snout aided in foraging activities

Front legs
Both validated species of Triceratops have extremely sturdy front legs to ensure support for its heavy head and chest cavity

Skull
Over 50 complete Triceratops skulls have been found today, each confirming that they were incredibly heavy and solid

Jaw
The Triceratops' teeth were arranged in groups of 36-40 columns in each side of the jaw, with three to five stacked teeth per column

The statistics...

Triceratops

Length: 8m (26ft)

Height: 2.9m (9.5ft)

Weight: 6,350kg (14,000lb)

Diet: Herbivore

Discovered: Colorado, USA

The fundamental diet of the Triceratops was largely dictated by – and most likely co-evolved with – its low-slung posture and head position, which was located close to the ground. As a consequence of these factors, as well as its deep and narrow beak and sharp teeth batteries, both species of Triceratops most likely consumed large amounts of low-growth ferns, palms and cycads, plucking the plants with their beaks and then shredding the fibrous material with their teeth.

The Triceratops' main potential predators were carnivorous theropod dinosaurs such as the Tyrannosaurus rex. However, while modern-day depictions of these two prehistoric titans are often far-fetched, Triceratops specimens have been discovered with T-rex bite marks and even one where the herbivore had had one of its brow horns snapped off entirely.

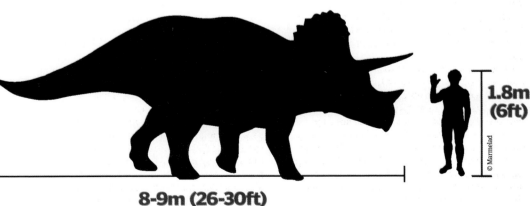

1.8m (6ft)

8-9m (26-30ft)

"Velociraptor hunting techniques revolved largely around their speed and agility"

Velociraptors

One of the most deadly dinosaurs, the Velociraptor was an adept predator and scavenger, but not quite the creature Hollywood would have us believe...

Velociraptors have been ingrained in public consciousness since the 1993 movie Jurassic Park showcased them as the most fearsome of apex predators. Smart, lethal and bloodthirsty, the Velociraptors of the film arguably stole the show. However, the movie was famed for its indulgence of artistic licence, with palaeontologists bemoaning the lack of historical accuracy.

So what were these dinosaurs really like? Velociraptor, of which there are two verified species – V mongoliensis and V osmolskae, was a genus of dromaeosaurid ("running lizard") theropod dinosaur that lived in the Late Cretaceous period, about 75-71 million years ago. They were two metres (6.6 feet) long, just under a metre (three feet) high, feathered and bipedal, running on two of their three toes per foot. Velociraptors were native to modern-day central Asia mst notably Mongolia), where they

built large, ground-based nests to protect their vulnerable young.

Velociraptors, though often living in close proximity to one another, were largely solitary and, while certain finds suggest they could have teamed up while chasing their quarry, they were not pack hunters, with evidence showing they would fight among themselves for feeding rights. In addition, their staple diet consisted of animals of equal size and weight to themselves or those smaller than them, with very little evidence suggesting they would attempt to bring down larger dinosaurs, such as the Tyrannosaurus rex à la Jurassic Park.

Velociraptor hunting techniques revolved largely around their speed and agility. They could accelerate up to 64 kilometres (40 miles) per hour and pounce long distances, as well as grip prey firmly with their unique, sickle-shaped claws (notably

their enlarged 'killing claw'). These traits were partnered with a tendency to ambush prey, rather than tackle their victims face on or from long range (see the 'Slash or subdue?' boxout for more). Interestingly, however, while there's no doubt that Velociraptors hunted live prey, unearthed fossilised evidence suggests they were also incredibly active scavengers, with the species frequently feeding on carrion (pterosaur bones have been found in velociraptor guts, for instance) and carcasses left over by other predators.

Velociraptors died out along with the remaining species of dromaeosauridae in the run up to, and as a result of, the Cretaceous-Tertiary mass-extinction event that occurred approximately 65.5 million years ago. Despite this, elements of their anatomy and appearance can still be seen today – albeit in heavily evolved forms – in many species of bird.

The statistics…

Velociraptor

Length: 2m (6.6ft)

Height: 0.8m (2.5ft)

Weight: 113kg (200lb)

Diet: Carnivore

Discovered: Mongolia

This is an accurate representation of a Velociraptor, being covered in feathers and attacking prey smaller than itself

Slash or subdue?

Did Velociraptors use their sickle-shaped claws to disembowel prey or for some other purpose?

The majority of non-avian theropod dinosaurs are characterised by razor-sharp serrated teeth and talon-like recurved claws, the Velociraptor being no exception. Armed with a bounty of claws on both its hands and feet, the Velociraptor at first glance seems to be the perfect killing machine, capable of rapidly chasing down prey before shredding their flesh with one of their knife-like tools. Well, that was at least the commonly accepted theory among palaeontologists until late in 2011, before a new study by a team of international dinosaur experts suggested an entirely different use for them.

The study suggested that far from their claws – specifically the Velociraptor's much-touted 'killing claws' – being used to shred and slice prey in order to kill them prior to consumption, they were far more likely to be used in a similar way to the talons of modern-day hawks and eagles. This entails the birds using their talons as a gripping tool, snaring prey of a lesser body size, pinning them down with their own body weight and then often consuming them live with their beaks.

This theory is seemingly backed up by the Velociraptor's feet showing morphology consistent with a grasping function, supporting a prey immobilisation model rather than the originally assumed combative one.

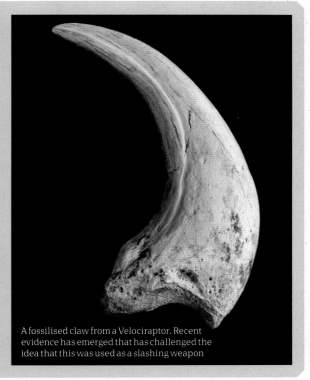

A fossilised claw from a Velociraptor. Recent evidence has emerged that has challenged the idea that this was used as a slashing weapon

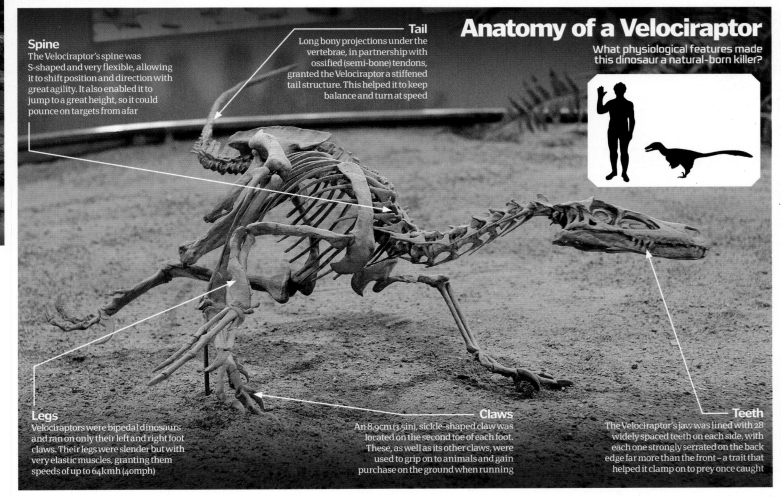

Anatomy of a Velociraptor

What physiological features made this dinosaur a natural-born killer?

Spine
The Velociraptor's spine was S-shaped and very flexible, allowing it to shift position and direction with great agility. It also enabled it to jump to a great height, so it could pounce on targets from afar

Tail
Long bony projections under the vertebrae, in partnership with ossified (semi-bone) tendons, granted the Velociraptor a stiffened tail structure. This helped it to keep balance and turn at speed

Legs
Velociraptors were bipedal dinosaurs and ran on only their left and right foot claws. Their legs were slender but with very elastic muscles, granting them speeds of up to 64kmh (40mph)

Claws
An 8.9cm (3.5in), sickle-shaped claw was located on the second toe of each foot. These, as well as its other claws, were used to grip on to animals and gain purchase on the ground when running

Teeth
The Velociraptor's jaw was lined with 28 widely spaced teeth on each side, with each one strongly serrated on the back edge far more than the front – a trait that helped it clamp on to prey once caught

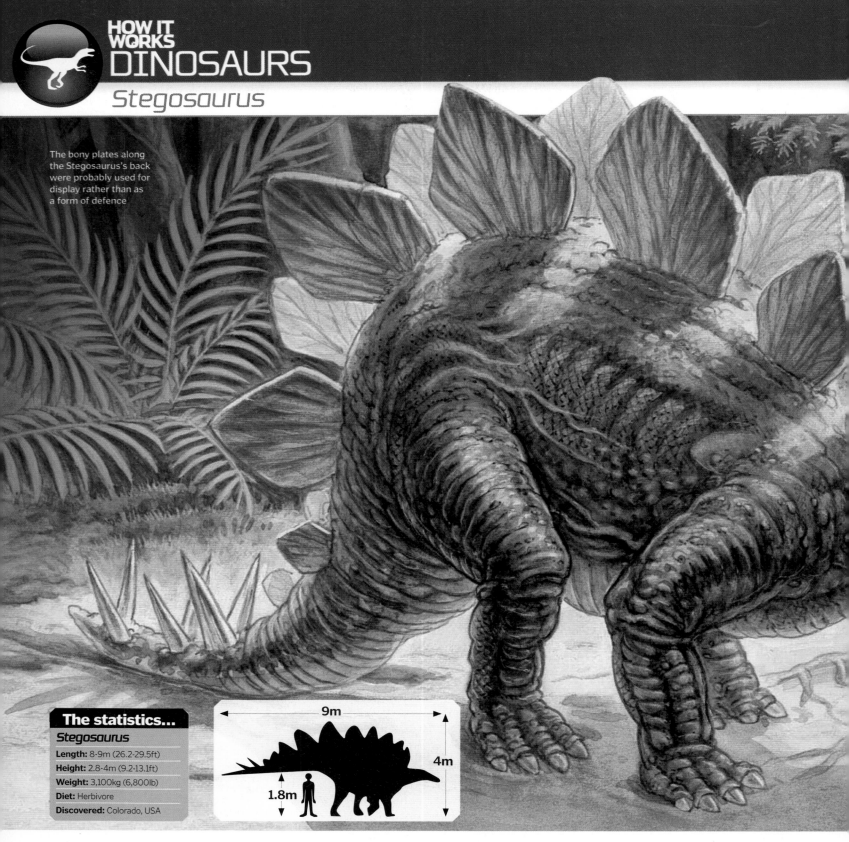

The bony plates along the Stegosaurus's back were probably used for display rather than as a form of defence

The statistics...

Stegosaurus

Length: 8-9m (26.2-29.5ft)

Height: 2.8-4m (9.2-13.1ft)

Weight: 3,100kg (6,800lb)

Diet: Herbivore

Discovered: Colorado, USA

9m

4m

1.8m

Skull

Despite its large scale, the Stegosaurus's head was very narrow and it had a tiny brain capacity

Stegosaurus

One of the most well known of the dinosaurs, the Stegosaurus boasted a series of diamond-shaped bone plates and a tail that could kill

Maybe the most iconic genus of dinosaurs ever excavated, the Stegosaurus was a herbivorous titan, capable of consuming huge quantities of low-level foliage while protecting itself from predators with its vast armoured frame and potentially lethal spiked tail.

The first example of Stegosaurus – from which its family name, Stegosauridae, derived – was unearthed in 1877 and since then four confirmed species of the dinosaur have been officially identified. Each species demonstrates a similar structure and feature set, with each animal epitomising a large quadruped, sporting a series of diamond-shaped plates along its back. These large creatures were over eight metres (26 feet) long and were heavily built at over 3,000 kilograms (6,614 pounds).

Interestingly, it's these plates that palaeontologists and academics know the least about, with a variety of arrangements, structures and uses suggested. When first unearthed it was speculated that they were used as a form of armoured defence against carnivorous predators. However, their positioning along the back and apparent bluntness has led to this theory being largely dismissed today. Instead, academics suggest that the plates were used as a decorative feature – perhaps in mating displays or to ward off Stegosaurus rivals in territory disputes.

The field of palaeobiology reveals almost everything else about this genus. Studying fossilised evidence it is clear that due to Stegosaurus's very small and narrow skull, they had a tiny brain and so were not very intelligent – something seemingly confirmed by their primitive and mundane feeding habits. The low level of the animal's neck, short but bulky forelegs and raised pelvis/elongated hind legs indicate that Stegosaurus spent much of its daily routine consuming large quantities of low-lying foliage (such as ferns, cycads and conifers). This is confirmed by the shape and formation of its teeth and a low bite force.

Upon closer inspection of the dinosaur's legs it is also clear that it could not move very quickly. This is apparent as the discrepancy in size between the front and hind legs is so great that, if the creature ran at over eight kilometres (five miles) per hour, its longer back legs would cross over the forelegs leading it to fall.

Despite these shortcomings, Stegosaurus wasn't totally defenceless, as it boasted a flexible, armour-plated and spiked tail. Taking Stegosaurus stenops as an example, the dinosaur had four dermal tail spikes of approximately 75 centimetres (29.5 inches) in length each, which extended out from the tail slightly off the horizontal plane. These spikes enabled the Stegosaurus to whip its tail and puncture the flesh of any attackers.

Stegosaurus anatomy
Understand the biological structure of this distinctive dino from the inside out

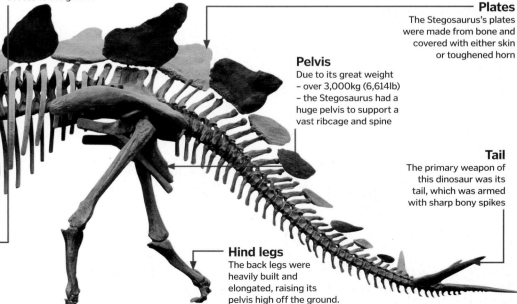

Forelegs
The forelegs were very bulky and powerful. They were relatively short, however, granting easy access to the ground

Plates
The Stegosaurus's plates were made from bone and covered with either skin or toughened horn

Pelvis
Due to its great weight – over 3,000kg (6,614lb) – the Stegosaurus had a huge pelvis to support a vast ribcage and spine

Tail
The primary weapon of this dinosaur was its tail, which was armed with sharp bony spikes

Neck
Due to its herbivorous diet, the neck angled downwards, allowing the animal to eat low-level vegetation easily

Hind legs
The back legs were heavily built and elongated, raising its pelvis high off the ground.

© Eva Kröcher; Alamy; Nobu Tamura

The statistics...

Tyrannosaurus rex

Length: 12-13m (40-43ft)

Height: 4m (13ft)

Weight: 6-9 tonnes

Diet: Carnivore

Discovered: Colorado, USA

Tyrannosaurus rex

Learn about the lizard king's physiology and how it presided over the prehistoric jungle

Tyrannosaurus rex was a species of Theropoda dinosaur in the Late Cretaceous period. Like other tyrannosaurids – such as Tarbosaurus and Gorgosaurus – the T-rex was a bipedal carnivore and apex predator and scavenger, preying on smaller dinosaurs directly or out-muscling them for their kills. Typical prey included hadrosaurs and ceratopsians.

Tyrannosaurus rex's name translates as "tyrant lizard king" – something that was historically attributed due to its immense size. Indeed, the Tyrannosaurus rex is one of the largest species ever excavated by palaeontologists, with specimens averaging over 12 metres (40 feet) in length and four metres (13 feet) in height, but it wasn't the biggest carnivorous dino. It was incredibly heavy with fully grown adults weighing up to nine tonnes; this figure was suggested in 2011 after an in-depth study which made digital 3D models of five T-rex skeletons.

Due to their considerable size, the Tyrannosaurus rex had very few, if any, predators – a fact that enabled it to remain unchallenged as the Late Cretaceous era's apex predator on land and to live for lengthy periods. Estimates taken from excavated specimens – of which there are now more than 30 confirmed around the world – indicate that the T-rex's life span was roughly 30 years, with the majority of growth taking place in the first 16 years before tailing off rapidly. This suggests that the Tyrannosaurus rex would have reached adulthood at approximately 20 years of age.

As with almost all species of Dinosauria, the Tyrannosaurus was wiped out 65.5 million years ago in the Cretaceous-Palaeogene (K-Pg) extinction event. At the time it was one of the last widespread non-avian dinosaurs, as evidenced by the discovery of many specimens throughout North America.

T-rex mythbuster

Due to a variety of films depicting the T-rex in their own unique way, an accurate view of the species has been clouded. For example, despite being a prominent star of all the Jurassic Park films, Tyrannosaurus rex did not exist in the Jurassic period (199-145 MYA). In fact, it lived millions of years later during the Late Cretaceous (100-65.5 MYA). Further, for decades T-rex has been depicted as having green scaly skin. However, recent evidence suggests its skin colour was varied and, during the early years of its life, it probably sported insulative feathers. The T-rex has also been commonly lauded as the biggest carnivorous dinosaur of them all. This isn't strictly true, with palaeontological evidence suggesting the species Spinosaurus outsized it by over three metres (9.9 feet) in length. And finally, another myth perpetuated in Jurassic Park is that the Tyrannosaurus could run at high speed (ie keep up with a car), but it could probably only manage about 40 kilometres (25 miles) per hour due to its relatively small strides.

Anatomy of the lizard king

We analyse a Tyrannosaurus rex's skeleton to see what made it such a deadly predator

Tail
Crucial for maintaining balance – especially as modern evidence suggests T-rex had a near-horizontal spinal position – the dinosaur's large tail was essential for chasing prey

Body cavity
The Tyrannosaurus rex had an incredibly heavy body structure and a wide body cavity. To improve mobility, some of the dinosaur's vertebrae had holes – helping to reduce weight

Skull
Tyrannosaurus's skull was huge and its snout and lower jaw were very deep. The eye sockets faced forward to a greater degree than most dinosaurs, indicating it had acute binocular vision

Hind legs
The large hind legs connected to the body via a lizard-style hip arrangement. The size of the legs granted the dinosaur excellent pushing power, though due to its small strides (compared to other species) it couldn't run very fast

Forelimbs
Tyrannosaurus had incredibly short forelimbs with hands boasting two full-sized fingers and a single smaller one. The two larger fingers were equipped with razor-sharp, sickle-shaped claws

Mouth
The T-rex's mouth was massive and contained 60 serrated teeth. All the teeth were different sizes, with some up to 20cm (7.9in) long

© Alamy; Thinkstock

The giant Brachiosaurus

Three times longer and two times taller than a double-decker bus, Brachiosaurus truly was a terrestrial titan of epic proportions

Brachiosaurus was a genus of sauropod dinosaur that roamed the Earth during the Late Jurassic period (circa 155-140 million years ago). They are characterised, like many sauropods of the time, by their huge necks and comparatively tiny skulls and brains. Currently only one species has been officially confirmed – B altithorax – though others have been suggested.

Interestingly, like other sauropods, these creatures – despite weighing an estimated 60 tons and measuring up to 30 metres (98 feet)

long – were actually colossal vegetarians, with their diet comprising solely foliage.

Their evolution of such a long neck (see 'The high life' boxout for more details) seems to be intrinsically linked to their diet, with the elevated head position enabling them to access leaves unavailable to shorter species.

This dominion over a food source is also a major factor behind their generally massive proportions, with millions of years of domination allowing them to grow to sizes far in excess of rival creatures from the same era.

The epic size of Brachiosaurus was also its primary form of defence when it came to predators. Once fully grown, their legs would have resembled tree trunks and these – partnered with a heavy, stocky tail – made them extremely difficult to tackle.

While their size and domination granted many benefits, it was also a contributor to Brachiosaurus's eventual demise, with resource depletion and climate change leading to their background extinction around 145 million years ago.

Anatomy of a titan
Take a look inside this lofty member of the dino family

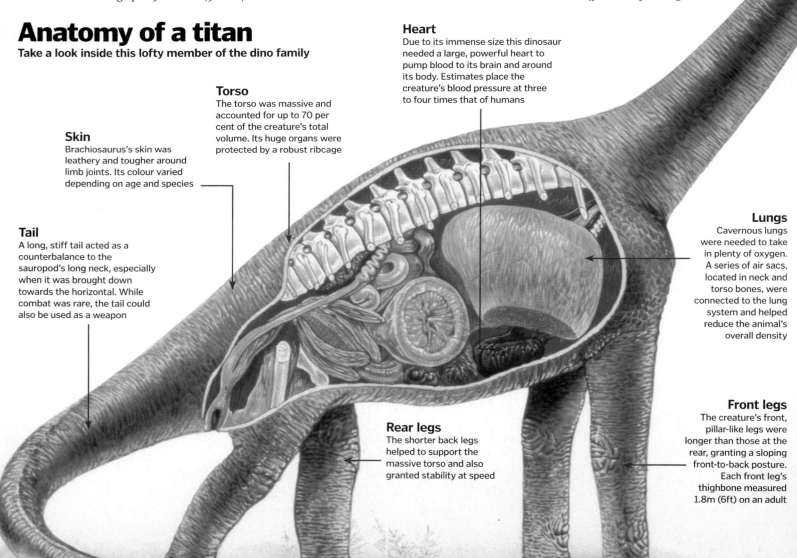

Heart
Due to its immense size this dinosaur needed a large, powerful heart to pump blood to its brain and around its body. Estimates place the creature's blood pressure at three to four times that of humans

Torso
The torso was massive and accounted for up to 70 per cent of the creature's total volume. Its huge organs were protected by a robust ribcage

Skin
Brachiosaurus's skin was leathery and tougher around limb joints. Its colour varied depending on age and species

Tail
A long, stiff tail acted as a counterbalance to the sauropod's long neck, especially when it was brought down towards the horizontal. While combat was rare, the tail could also be used as a weapon

Lungs
Cavernous lungs were needed to take in plenty of oxygen. A series of air sacs, located in neck and torso bones, were connected to the lung system and helped reduce the animal's overall density

Rear legs
The shorter back legs helped to support the massive torso and also granted stability at speed

Front legs
The creature's front, pillar-like legs were longer than those at the rear, granting a sloping front-to-back posture. Each front leg's thighbone measured 1.8m (6ft) on an adult

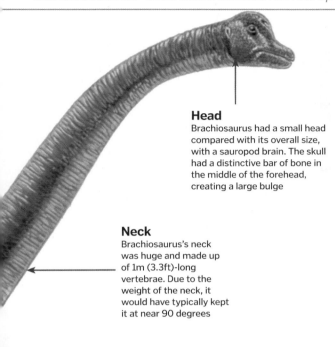

Head
Brachiosaurus had a small head compared with its overall size, with a sauropod brain. The skull had a distinctive bar of bone in the middle of the forehead, creating a large bulge

Neck
Brachiosaurus's neck was huge and made up of 1m (3.3ft)-long vertebrae. Due to the weight of the neck, it would have typically kept it at near 90 degrees

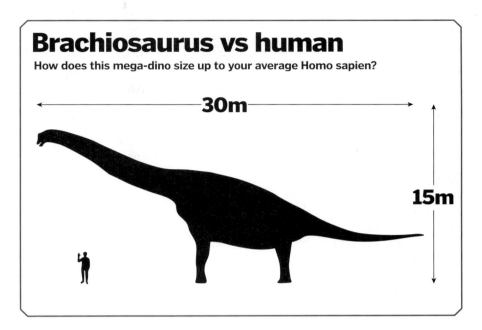

Brachiosaurus vs human
How does this mega-dino size up to your average Homo sapien?

← **30m** →

15m

The statistics...
Brachiosaurus

Length: 25-30m (82-98ft)
Height: 15m (49ft)
Weight: 60 tons
Diet: Herbivore
Discovered: Colorado, USA

The high life
Each vertebra in the neck of Brachiosaurus was approximately one metre (3.3 feet) in length, which is absolutely colossal compared with the largest animals around today. Combined, these vertebrae formed an extensive, snake-like neck that enabled the Brachiosaurus to reach up into tall trees and other plants with ease to feed on foliage – of which it needed vast quantities to survive.

Importantly, despite the long neck giving Brachiosaurus a keen browsing advantage when compared with other smaller dinosaurs, as a payoff it would have needed a near-vertical neck posture most of the time in order to prevent injury.

Unlike the popular 20th-century view that Brachiosaurus would raise and lower its head to access different tiers of foliage, it is now generally thought that only the immediate level around its head height would have been eaten, with lower tiers of leaves only consumed by juveniles.

Its name translates as 'arm lizard' because unusually for dinosaurs its front legs were longer than its hind legs

© Alamy/Getty

Ankylosaurus

A club-wielding brute of a creature, this tough dino had the power to break bones

Ankylosaurus was one of the largest ankylosaurs, a genus of armoured dinosaurs that lived throughout North America between 75 and 65.5 million years ago. Famous for both its brutal tail-mounted club and its immense bone plate armour, the Ankylosaurus was a defensive titan, capable of fending off rivals many times its size.

Ankylosaurus's focus on defence was born out of its herbivorous nature, with its entire body geared towards the consumption of foliage. From its low-slung body, rows of leaf-shaped cropping teeth, short front legs, wide feet and cavernous stomach, the Ankylosaurus was the consummate browser,

devouring vegetation whole with little shredding or chewing. Indeed, studies have indicated that the skull and jaw of the Ankylosaurus were structurally tougher than many similar, contemporary dinosaurs.

In fact, evidence suggests that Ankylosaurus – and ankylosaurs in general – were adept survivors. But despite their impressive armour, weaponry and sustainable diet, they could not cope with the Cretaceous-Tertiary extinction event that wiped out all terrestrial dinosaurs approximately 65.5 million years ago. Only a few fossils of this prehistoric herbivore have been excavated to date – most coming from the Hell Creek Formation in Montana, USA.

Club members only

The well-known tail club of the Ankylosaurus was one of the most lethal weapons sported by any dinosaur. The club was made from several large bone plates called osteoderms that were fused into the last few vertebrae of the animal's tail. Behind these vertebrae several others lined with thick, partially ossified tendons completed the club's handle, resulting in a structure that, when swung, was capable of dealing out a lot of damage. Indeed, a study in 2009 suggested that the tail clubs of fully grown ankylosaurs could easily crush and break bone with a force capable of caving in an assailant's skull. Whether or not the animal purposely aimed the club to cause damage remains unclear at this point.

As well as a weapon, the tail might also have played a role in sexual selection

Ankylosaurus anatomy
Get to know the key biology of this tank-like dino

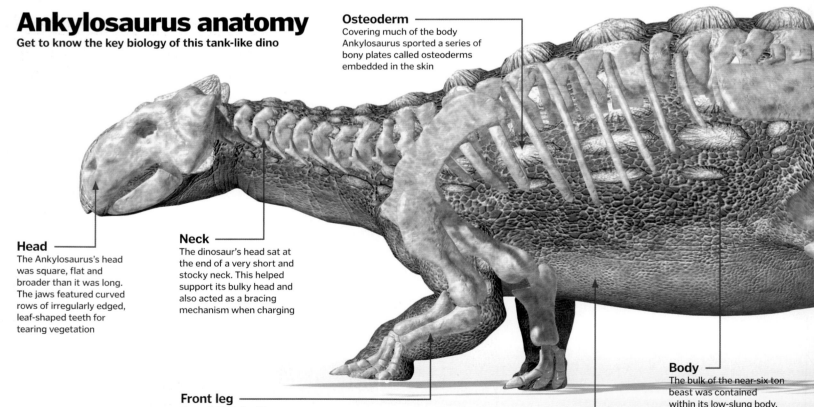

Osteoderm
Covering much of the body Ankylosaurus sported a series of bony plates called osteoderms embedded in the skin

Head
The Ankylosaurus's head was square, flat and broader than it was long. The jaws featured curved rows of irregularly edged, leaf-shaped teeth for tearing vegetation

Neck
The dinosaur's head sat at the end of a very short and stocky neck. This helped support its bulky head and also acted as a bracing mechanism when charging

Front leg
Powerful but short legs supported the front half of the animal. The wide foot area of these forelegs granted good traction and stability

Stomach
The only part of the dinosaur that was unarmoured, the underbelly hung low to the ground. Predators would try to tip Ankylosaurus over to access this weak point

Body
The bulk of the near-six ton beast was contained within its low-slung body. This was covered with armoured bone plating and topped with spines

You shall not pass!

The impressive, almost bulletproof armour of the Ankylosaurus was not magic but rather a series of interlocking bone plates called osteoderms. These bone plates, which were locked into the skin, were bone overlaid with a tough layer of keratin. The plates were located over most of the body, but were not uniform in shape nor size, with some resembling flat diamonds – as seen on crocodiles and armadillos today – and others appearing like circular nodules. The addition of these plates on top of the Ankylosaurus's head, along with a set of pyramidal horns to its rear and a row of triangular spikes mounted to each side of the tail club meant that attacking this creature – even if you were an apex predator like the T-rex – was not a good idea.

Ankylosaurus was tough enough to go up against the most fearsome dinosaurs and come out on top

Spine
At key areas Ankylosaurus also sported bony spines for extra protection or – in the case of those mounted to the side of the tail club – greater offensive capabilities

Club
The characteristic tail club of Ankylosaurus was made from numerous osteoderms, each fused to the last few vertebrae of the tail

> "Ankylosaurus's focus on defence was born out of its herbivorous nature"

Tail
A medium-sized tail – also armoured with bone plates – helped balance the weighty Ankylosaurus and provided the power to cause maximum damage with its club

Rear leg
Equally powerful – if not more so – but longer than the Ankylosaurus's forelegs, the rear legs reached up to about 1.7m (5.6ft) at the hip

Ankylosaurus vs human
How would this dino have sized up to a person?

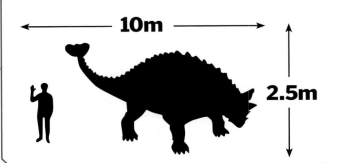

10m

2.5m

Ribs
Apatosaurus possessed incredibly long, robust ribs compared to most other diplodocids, granting it an unusually deep chest cavity

Head
Apatosaurus had a deep, slender skull filled with long peg-like teeth. These broad, rounded teeth were excellent at stripping off leaves from branches

Torso
A colossal torso that weighed many tonnes was standard containing similarly huge organs, including a 500-litre, four-chambered heart and two 900-litre capacity lungs

Neck
As with other sauropods, the Apatosaurus's neck vertebrae were deeply bifurcated, carrying paired spines. The neck was also filled with many weight-saving air sacs

Meet the real Brontosaurus

One of the largest animals to ever exist on Earth, the Apatosaurus towered metres over its Jurassic rivals

Around four times heavier than an African elephant, five times longer than your car and almost six times the height of a full-grown human, Apatosaurus was one of the largest dinosaurs of the Jurassic era and one of most gigantic to ever walk the Earth.

As is typical with large dinosaurs of this period, Apatosaurus (once mistakenly known as Brontosaurus) was a herbivore, consuming vast quantities of foliage and grasses over the lands that now form modern-day North America. Interestingly, despite its size, its name is derived from the Greek 'apate' and 'saurus', which translate as 'deception lizard' – a name bestowed by its original discoverer, American palaeontologist Othniel Charles Marsh.

Prior to the 1970s, Apatosaurus, along with many other sauropods, were considered largely aquatic creatures that relied on being partially submerged in swamps and lakes to remain stable – a view seemingly confirmed by their colossal bulk. However, recent evidence has demonstrated that through a combination of massive limb bones and a series of weight-reducing internal air sacs located throughout the neck and spine, Apatosaurus's home was, in fact, entirely land-based, only spending time at water sources to drink.

Speaking of drinking, the Apatosaurus required gallons of water per day to remain healthy, while it also needed to process vast amounts of food, spending a large proportion of each day grazing. It did this with few predators, as only the largest carnivorous dinosaurs had any chance of bringing down an Apatosaurus, largely thanks to its size. It also had a deadly weapon in its tail, which was capable of being swung at great velocity at any foes.

Despite its defensive prowess, however, the Apatosaurus could not battle off extinction, with it falling to a medium-sized extinction event around 150 million years ago.

Apatosaurus vs human
How would this enormous dinosaur have sized up to a person?

23m

9m

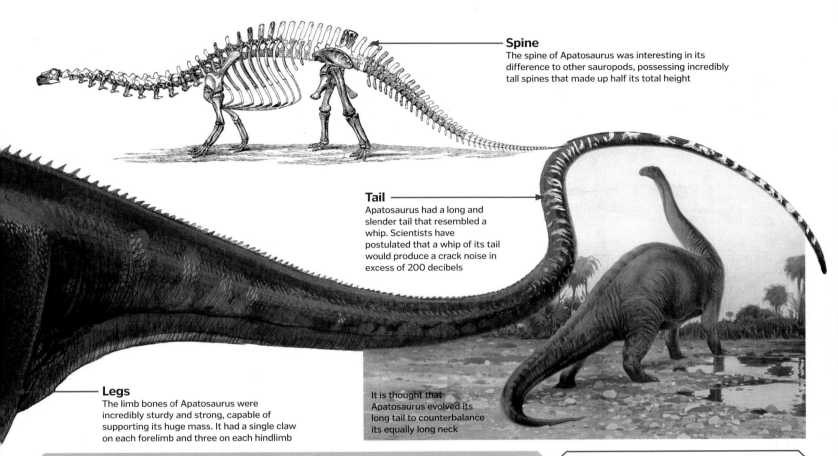

Spine
The spine of Apatosaurus was interesting in its difference to other sauropods, possessing incredibly tall spines that made up half its total height

Tail
Apatosaurus had a long and slender tail that resembled a whip. Scientists have postulated that a whip of its tail would produce a crack noise in excess of 200 decibels

Legs
The limb bones of Apatosaurus were incredibly sturdy and strong, capable of supporting its huge mass. It had a single claw on each forelimb and three on each hindlimb

It is thought that Apatosaurus evolved its long tail to counterbalance its equally long neck

The bone wars

During the beginning of the golden age of modern palaeontology, two prominent American palaeontologists, Edward Cope and Othniel Marsh, had a falling out over excavated dinosaur remains, with the men then proceeding to attempt to beat each other to unearth and describe new species of dinosaur. In this rush to become the foremost palaeontogist of the age, Marsh described first in 1877 and then later in 1879 two supposedly separate species of dinosaur. He named the first one Apatosaurus and called the second one Brontosaurus.

Following this, the name of Brontosaurus became world famous, with a complete skeleton mounted and displayed in the Peabody Museum, Yale, under the Marsh title in 1905. However, Marsh in his haste had made a terrible mistake. The Brontosaurus was actually just a fully-grown Apatosaurus and, since the Apatosaurus had been described first in 1877, its name took precedent, with 'Brontosaurus' made officially redundant in the early-20th century. Interestingly, however, as the Brontosaurus name had become firmly fixed in the public consciousness, it remained far more popular and is still in use to this day to the chagrin of many dinosaur experts.

A photograph of Othniel Marsh taken between 1865 and 1880

Stamp scandal

In 1989, the US Post Office decided to release a special edition set of four stamps depicting famous dinosaurs. These included a Tyrannosaurus, Stegosaurus, Pteranodon and, interestingly, a Brontosaurus.

The latter was included despite the fact that, as noted in 'The bone wars' boxout, the name 'Brontosaurus' had been made officially redundant in the early-20th century.

The fallout from this was massive, with many palaeontologists and dinosaur enthusiasts accusing the US Post Office of promoting 'scientific illiteracy' and re-opened a bone war-style feud between others. Indeed, even the celebrated palaeontologist Stephen Jay Gould got involved, writing a famous defence of the Brontosaurus name in his Natural History magazine piece 'Bully for Brontosaurus'.

Marine reptiles

Discover the creatures that ruled and dominated the prehistoric waters

Pliosaurs

These marine reptiles were built to hunt deep

Pliosaurs were large carnivorous marine reptiles that mainly inhabited the waters around Europe in the Jurassic and Cretaceous periods. Their diet consisted of fish, sea-based dinosaurs and other marine reptiles.

The two most well known varieties of pliosaur are the Kronosaurus and the Liopleurodon. The Kronosaurus was known to have stalked the seas around Australia and South America in the late Cretaceous period and measured up to nine meters (30ft) in length. Liopleurodons measured a colossal 12 meters (39ft) in length. Resembling a whale, it was a highly manoeuvrable creature that was capable of swimming at all depths.

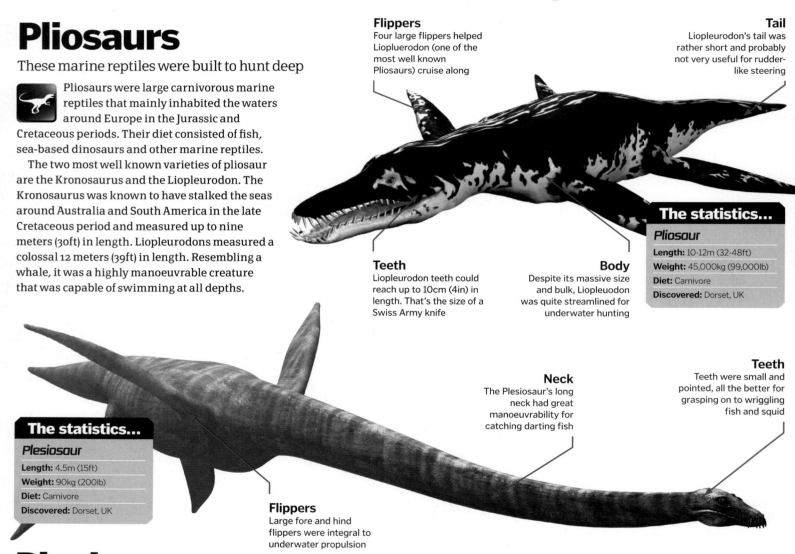

Flippers
Four large flippers helped Liopluerodon (one of the most well known Pliosaurs) cruise along

Tail
Liopleurodon's tail was rather short and probably not very useful for rudder-like steering

Teeth
Liopleurodon teeth could reach up to 10cm (4in) in length. That's the size of a Swiss Army knife

Body
Despite its massive size and bulk, Liopleuodon was quite streamlined for underwater hunting

The statistics...
Pliosaur
Length: 10-12m (32-48ft)
Weight: 45,000kg (99,000lb)
Diet: Carnivore
Discovered: Dorset, UK

Neck
The Plesiosaur's long neck had great manoeuvrability for catching darting fish

Teeth
Teeth were small and pointed, all the better for grasping on to wriggling fish and squid

The statistics...
Plesiosaur
Length: 4.5m (15ft)
Weight: 90kg (200lb)
Diet: Carnivore
Discovered: Dorset, UK

Flippers
Large fore and hind flippers were integral to underwater propulsion

Plesiosaurs

These powerful reptiles were every inch the aquatic version of a dinosaur

Plesiosaurs were part of marine ecology from the late Triassic period to the end of the Cretaceous period and were powerful swimmers that could strike fast-moving prey with efficiency. Plesiosaurs typically had a stocky torso, four large flippers, a long neck and a small skull with small, pointed teeth and one such example was the Plesiosaurus, which inhabited the shallow seas of Europe during the early Jurassic period.

Measuring anywhere between 3-5 meters in length, the Plesiosaurus was one of the very first prehistoric reptiles to be discovered and the fossil remains pointed very much towards a powerful creature that was build to cope with its precise fish-catching feeding habits. With a forward burst of the flippers on one side of its body coupled with backwards thrust of the flippers on the other side could turn the Plesiosaurus on a sixpence, its relatively weak, stumpy tail acting as a rudder to steer it. It was such agility that the helped the plesiosaurs dominate the ecosystem as no unsuspecting fish would have been able to escape it.

Ichthyosaurs

Few marine creatures could outrun these 'fish lizards'

Ichthyosaurs inhabited much of the Earth's seas and oceans during the mid-Triassic to late Cretaceous periods. To date there are more than 80 recorded species of Ichthyosaur, with more being added regularly. Although some bared a physical resemblance to modern day dolphins or sharks, skeletally they were more closely linked to reptiles – in fact Ichthyosaur translates as 'fish lizard'.

Ichthyosaurs ranged vastly in size, with the smallest (the Chaohusaurus) measuring in at around 70cm and the largest (as yet unnamed) was found in Canada and is believed to measure in the region of 23 meters in length. A typical ichthyosaur was the Ichthyosaurus, which frequented the waters around the British Isles during the early Jurassic period and measured two meters in length. Designed for speed with four flippers (in the hands and feet positions), a paddle-like tail and a dorsal fin, the Ichthyosaurus hunted mainly fish, its elongated skull and rows of sharp teeth ideal for catching slippery prey. It is thought that the smooth, Dolphin-like torso of the Ichthyosaurs could see them swim at speeds of up to 45kph, their powerful bodies being able to maintain that top speed for up to half an hour.

Dorsal fin
Not all species of Ichthyosaur had a dorsal fin, but it is believed that many types did

Teeth
The Ichthyosaur often had conical teeth to assist with catching smaller prey

Flippers
The Ichthyosaur had flippers which contained a large number of digits and phalanges

The statistics...
Ichthyosaur
Length: Up to 16m (52ft)
Weight: 930kg (2090lb)
Diet: Carnivore
Discovered: Dorset, UK

Mosasaurs

Introducing the T-Rex of the seas...

Mosasaurs lived in the late Cretaceous period and were the true giants of the sea. Some mosasaurs, such as the Hainosaurus, could reach lengths of up to 17 meters, their huge frames typically spent swimming slowly along the sea beds stalking slow-moving prey such as ammonites and turtles. However, as mosasaurs could breathe air, seabirds were also part of their ecosystem. Possessing two sets of conical teeth, mosasaurs used rocks and underwater plantation as cover to close in on their prey and then strike quickly. Some skeletal remains indicate that they were susceptible to attacks by shark-like predators.

The first mosasaur remains were uncovered around the 1770s in an underground mine near Maastricht, Holland, on the Meuse River. Fossil skin impressions indicate that they possessed scaly skin similar to that of a snake.

The statistics...
Mosasaur
Length: Up to 17m (56ft)
Weight: Up to 20 tonnes
Diet: Carnivore
Discovered: Maastricht, Netherlands

Jaw
Most mosasaurs had a double jaw which allowed them to eat their prey in one go

Snake-like
In 1869 it was suggested that mosasaurs shared common ancestry with snakes, who coined the term Pythonomorpha to unite them

Eating habits
The larger mosasaurs were the kings of the Late Cretaceous seas, feeding on fish and ammonites

Plesiosaurus

We turn the spotlight on a ferocious marine reptile that dominated Earth's oceans throughout the Early Jurassic

Streamlined
A muscular torso allows
for great propulsion

The statistics...

Plesiosaurus

Length: 4.5m (15ft)	
Neck vertebrae: 40	
Weight: 90kg (200lb)	
Diet: Carnivore; eg fish, squid	
Discovered: Dorset, UK	

Plesiosaurus was an unusual long-necked marine reptile that lived in the Early Jurassic period (circa 199-175 million years ago).

This member of the sauropterygian superorder measured in at approximately 4.5 metres (15 feet) in length, sported a muscular and stocky body, a long and narrow neck, plus a short, stubby tail. Four large flipper-like limbs that attached in pairs to the torso allowed the creature to propel itself through the water at great speed, while a small head packed with rows of sharp, curved teeth ensured that once it got hold of its dinner there was no getting away.

Despite the reptile's underwater dominance, the Plesiosaurus could not in fact breathe underwater like fish so had to surface to draw in air. Due to its size, however, it could spend a considerable length of time submerged, allowing it to repeatedly dart through shoals of fish and squid while hunting.

Plesiosaurus inhabited the shallow seas of what is now Europe, dominating the waters due to its size, agility and ferocity. Early in their history, this domination reached new heights when the order split-evolved into two main lineages: Pliosaurs and Plesiosaurids. The former developed a shorter neck and elongated head, while the latter developed a snake-like neck of epic proportions. This divergence allowed the species in each lineage to prey on an increasingly varied range of creatures, with some giants, such as Pliosaurus funkei (formerly 'Predator X'), even capable of attacking other Plesiosaurs.

Plesiosaurus became extinct at the opening of the Middle Jurassic period (175 MYA), being superseded by its larger, more dominant relatives, like the Elasmosaurus. The Plesiosauria order, however, survived much longer, thriving worldwide until the Cretaceous-Tertiary (K-T) extinction event.

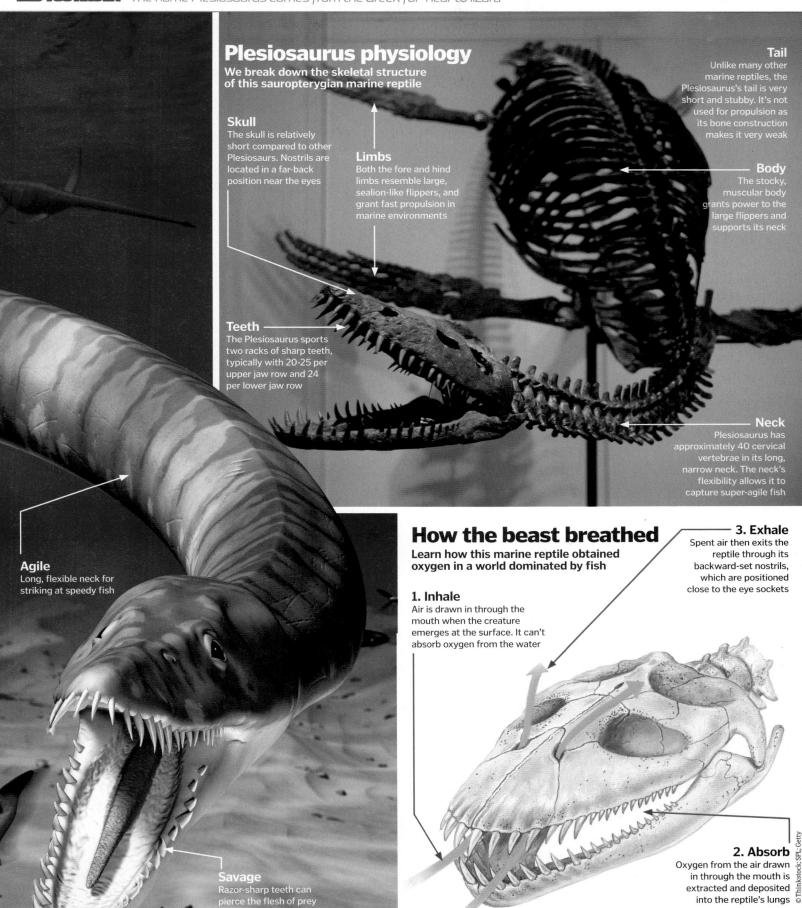

Plesiosaurus physiology
We break down the skeletal structure of this sauropterygian marine reptile

Skull
The skull is relatively short compared to other Plesiosaurs. Nostrils are located in a far-back position near the eyes

Limbs
Both the fore and hind limbs resemble large, sealion-like flippers, and grant fast propulsion in marine environments

Teeth
The Plesiosaurus sports two racks of sharp teeth, typically with 20-25 per upper jaw row and 24 per lower jaw row

Tail
Unlike many other marine reptiles, the Plesiosaurus's tail is very short and stubby. It's not used for propulsion as its bone construction makes it very weak

Body
The stocky, muscular body grants power to the large flippers and supports its neck

Neck
Plesiosaurus has approximately 40 cervical vertebrae in its long, narrow neck. The neck's flexibility allows it to capture super-agile fish

Agile
Long, flexible neck for striking at speedy fish

Savage
Razor-sharp teeth can pierce the flesh of prey

How the beast breathed
Learn how this marine reptile obtained oxygen in a world dominated by fish

1. Inhale
Air is drawn in through the mouth when the creature emerges at the surface. It can't absorb oxygen from the water

3. Exhale
Spent air then exits the reptile through its backward-set nostrils, which are positioned close to the eye sockets

2. Absorb
Oxygen from the air drawn in through the mouth is extracted and deposited into the reptile's lungs

© Thinkstock; SPL; Getty

093

Fly away
The discovery of embryo pterosaurs has lead scientists to believe they could fly from birth due to well-deveoped wing membrane

Discovery
The first pterosaur was discovered by Italian naturalist Cosimo Alessandro Collini in 1784

Two groups
Pterosaurs are made up of two groups: the earlier rhamphorhynchoids and the later pterodactyloids

Pterosaurs

Whatever you do, don't call them 'flying dinosaurs'

These flying reptiles lived alongside dinosaurs in a variety of environments across the Earth from the Late Triassic to the end of the Cretaceous period (225 to 65 million years ago). They ranged in size from just a few centimetres to more than 12 metres (one inch-39 feet), mostly feeding on fish while some scavenged dead animals and ate insects inland.

The wing of the pterosaur was unique, a large membrane suspended from a hugely expanded fourth finger. Pterosaurs are largely regarded as the first vertebrates to achieve sustainable powered flight, although the largest relied mainly on the wind and gliding to stay in the air. There is much contention among palaeontologists as to whether these flying reptiles should be classed as dinosaurs, but the

physical similarities are plain to see nonetheless, which is why we have included them here.

The Quetzalcoatlus is the largest of the pterosaurs–in fact it is the largest known flying animal of all time. With a wingspan of up to 12m (39 feet) and a head the size of a car, the Quetzalcoatlus ruled the sky in the Late Cretaceous period (100 to 65 million years ago). It is widely believed that Quetzalcoatlus fed on living dinosaurs, unlike other pterosaurs who preferred fish and dead animals, to fuel its enormous metabolic needs. Despite its incredible size this giant reptile weighed no more than 250kg (550lb) due to the hollow bones associated with pterosaurs.

Pterosaurs faced extinction after more than 150 million years at the same time as the dinosaurs, conquering every single continent in the process.

Tupandactylus imperator had a large crest on its head

Flying with wings

The hollow bones of the pterosaurs led many scientists to believe that their wings could not produce the power needed to achieve flight from a standstill without wind assistance. Recent fossil evidence has indicated that smaller pterosaurs could achieve sustainable flight, although the larger creatures still struggled to get airborne without help.

© H Zell

Pterodactylus

The Pterodactylus is arguably the most famous pterosaur. Its iconic features were characteristic of many pterosaurs, although a longer neck and a shorter tail ensured it was more suited to flight than its earlier ancestors, the rhamphorhynchoids.

Feet
Fossil evidence of feet with long claws indicates early pterosaurs lived on rocks and in treetops

Walk, don't run
Early pterosaurs struggled to walk with their wings closely attached to their legs

Head
The skulls of pterosaurs acted as a rudder in flight, with some later evolving rich ornamentation on top to attract mates

© Nobu Tamura

This little pinky
Their wings were suspended from elongated fourth digits and joined to their legs and their body

Hollow bones
Pterosaurs were very light and able to fly thanks to their hollow bones filled with air sacs

Size
With its wingspan and body measuring over a metre, pterodactylus was not the largest pterosaur

Mouth
The long jaws allowed it to hunt fish, using its small teeth to grab them out of the water

These giant creatures fed on fish and scavenged animals

© Thinkstock

Quetzalcoatlus

Discover more about the mysterious serpent of the sky and the largest flying vertebrate of all time

Not a great deal is actually known about this pterosaur that dates back to the late Cretaceous period, as only fragments have ever been discovered. However, evidence suggests that the Quetzalcoatlus possibly boasted a wingspan of up to 12m – making it the largest flying vertebrate of all time. But, despite its colossal size, its weight has been suggested could have been as low as 190lbs, but certainly no more than 550lbs. This was perhaps down to a complex system of air sacs situated inside many of the creature's bones that kept its weight down so as to be able to stay airborne for longer.

The Quetzalcoatlus's long, narrow wings made it an excellent glider, and while initial reports suggested that it could have used this skill to hover over water and scour the oceans for prey, it is now believed that it lived inland. The Quetzalcoatlus would have used rising thermals to glide high above the land, its keen eyes spotting prey from long distances like a modern day vulture – prey that consisted of vertebrates of all sizes. Thanks to its long neck and sharp, toothless jaws, the Quetzalcoatlus would have been able to probe deep inside large carcasses to devour the contents in order to fuel its gigantic metabolic requirements.

So far, fragments of the Quetzalcoatlus have only been found in Texas, North America, but it would be safe to assume that they were well equipped to traverse far further afield. Putting things into perspective, the next flying reptile down on the size scale, the Pteranodon, boasted a wingspan of 7m, a whole five meters shy of the Quetzalcoatlus (whose span would dwarf many small planes). More extensive remains of Pteranodons have been found as far afield as Europe and North America (England and Kansas, to be precise).

So while not as famous as some of the other species of winged reptiles, Quetzalcoatlus has emerged to be something of a winged wonder amongst the pterosaurs. A creature that steered a course inland away from its sea-scouting Pteranodon peers (the fragment remains were discovered about 400 kilometers inland from the nearest coastline and away from any large rivers or lakes present in the area during the Cretaceous period) to survive on a diet of small vertebrates and the discarded remains of other larger dinosaurs. And with new theories emerging regularly as to how the creature lived, it appears that the Quetzalcoatlus isn't quite ready to give up all of its secrets yet.

Quetzalcoatlus in flight
Quetzalcoatlus may have formed breeding colonies, like modern Albatrosses

The statistics...

Quetzalcoatlus

Height: 5m (18ft)

Wingspan: 10-12m (32-39ft)

Weight: 135kg (300lb)

Diet: Carnivore

Discovered: Texas, USA

Eyes
The keen eyes of the Quetzalcoatlus would have been able to spot land-based prey from long distances like a modern day bird of prey

Beak
Although initially believed to be blunt, the beak of the Quetzalcoatlus was later discovered to be long and pointed

Jaws
The long, toothless, jaws of the Quetzalcoatlus were well suited to probing the carcasses of dead dinosaurs

Skull
The Quetzalcoatlus had a skull measuring 2.5 meters, the majority of which was reserved for its long beak

Bones
Many of the Quetzalcoatlus's bones contained a complex series of air sacs that kept the creature's weight down considerably

Neck
The structure of the Quetzalcoatlus's neck vertebrae show that it was highly flexible – ideal for scouring the land below for prey

Wings
With a span of 12m, the Quetzalcoatlus's wings were long and narrow – perfect for gliding over long distances and making quick descents

Height: **5m (18ft)**
Wingspan: **10-12m (32-39ft)**

© Dk Images

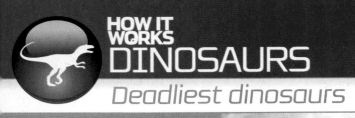
10
deadliest dinosaurs

Counting down the fiercest, most terrifying beasts that ever lived

Tyrannosaurus rex

Tyrannosaurus rex ("tie-RAN-a-SORE-uss rex") needs no introduction; its reputation as the ultimate carnivore and most badass dinosaur ever to roam the Earth precedes it. Tyrannosaurus rex (T-rex for short) literally means "tyrant lizard king", and there can be no doubt that it lived up to its name.

Standing at over five metres (16.4 feet) tall and 12 metres (39.4 feet) long, and weighing a staggering seven tonnes (15,400 pounds), the T-rex was once thought to have been the largest terrestrial carnivore in history, but subsequent discoveries of fellow titans Carcharodontosaurus, Giganotosaurus and Spinosaurus challenged this.

The T-rex walked on a pair of powerful hind legs and could run as fast as a professional footballer, but balance issues meant that Giganotosaurus could outrun it. Its brain was twice the size of most other predatory giants, but its intellectual prowess wasn't a patch on that of raptors like Utahraptor. So how does T-rex manage to cling to its crown?

It may not have been the biggest, fastest, heaviest, or smartest, but the king was the ultimate all-rounder. Its extraordinary sense of smell allowed T-rex to track prey over long distances and sniff out abandoned carcasses to scavenge. And then there is its not-so-secret weapon: its phenomenal bite, which was stronger than that of any land animal that ever lived. Its bone-splintering jaws chomped down with a force almost as huge as its own body weight, bringing to bear its 60 saw-edged conical teeth. Other dinosaurs had to close their mouth around prey multiple times to bring it down; T-rex only had to bite once.

Height: **5.6m (18.4ft)**
Length: **12m (39.4ft)**

"T-rex's phenomenal bite was stronger than that of any land animal that ever lived"

Killer stats

Tyrannosaurus Rex

The most efficient killing machine that ever lived, this awesome predator hunted indiscriminately on the floodplains of North America at the end of the Cretaceous period, 67-66 million years ago.

Size:	8/10
Arsenal & Adaptations:	8/10
Intellect:	7/10
Killer Rating:	10/10

Utahraptor

The mighty Utahraptor ("YOU-tah-RAP-tor") was three times larger and meaner than its cousin, the Velociraptor. Armed with a 30-centimetre (12-inch)-long sickle-shaped claw on each hind foot, it would kick, rip and tear its prey to death. Its leg bones were unusually thick, in order to support the powerful muscles dedicated to repeatedly driving the killing claw into its prey. In keeping with its smaller raptor cousins, it's possible that Utahraptor hunted in packs, like terrible three-metre (9.8-foot)-tall 500-kilogram (1,100-pound) wolves, and targeted prey many times larger than itself.

Height: **3m (9.8ft)**
Length: **6.5m (21.3ft)**

Height: **1m (3.3ft)**
Length: **1.8m (5.9ft)**

Velociraptor

Star of the infamous kitchen scene in Jurassic Park, the curious creature with the deadly curved toe claw has been terrorising nightmares for two decades. The film may have overstated their size and stripped them of their feathers, but it did get some things right: Velociraptors ("vel-OSS-e-RAP-tors") were fast and polished predators that oozed agility and intelligence, and may have hunted in packs.

Height: **3.6m (11.8ft)**
Length: **13m (42.7ft)**

Mapusaurus

A close cousin and look-alike of Giganotosarus, Mapusaurus ("MAH-puh-SORE-uss") hunted some of the largest dinosaurs that ever lived – the 35-metre (115-foot)-long herbivore Argentinosaurus. Its narrow blade-like teeth were ideal slicing tools, and the discovery of bones from several individuals found in one place has experts speculating that they formed groups or hunted in packs for extra lethality.

Brain
Record brain-to-body-weight ratio suggests it was the quickest-thinking and most intelligent of all known dinosaurs

Lightweight body structure
Slender and with a rod-like tail, Troodon was swift and nimble on its feet

Feathers?
Experts speculate that cool-climate-dwelling Troodon may have sported feathers for insulation

Eyes
Large and forward facing, giving it excellent stereoscopic vision and perhaps even the ability to see at night

Fingers
A semi-opposable finger on each hand meant it had the dexterity to grab and snare small mammals and reptiles

Claw
A retractable sickle-shaped claw on each foot was used for slashing and kicking at captured prey

Killer stats

Troodon
This diminutive dinosaur used cunning and cooperation to slay supposedly superior beasts in the wilds of North America during the Late Cretaceous Era, 74-65 million years ago.

Size:	3/10
Arsenal & Adaptations:	8/10
Intellect:	10/10
Killer Rating:	8/10

Troodon

Deadliness doesn't always come down to bulk and bite force. Troodon ("TROH-oh-don") – standing just 1.3 metres (4.3 feet) tall and weighing in at 40 kilograms (88 pounds) – was a wily whippet that made up for its lack of brawn with a whole lot of brain. In fact, it had the highest brain-to-body-weight ratio of any known dinosaur. Not only that; reconstructions of its brain have revealed nascent signs of folding – where more neural cells are packed into the same area for more efficient brain functioning – making it the most neurologically advanced specimen too.

The shape of fossilised skull remains suggest it possessed huge orb-like eyes that gave it superior vision – as well as the ability to see in low-lighting conditions and hunt nocturnally – and its slight frame made it extremely fleet of foot. While they may have been dwarfed by many of the behemoths on this list, a pack of alert and agile Troodons hunting as a pack could easily have brought down much bigger animals.

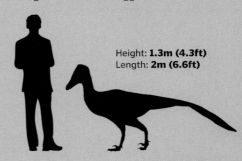

Height: **1.3m (4.3ft)**
Length: **2m (6.6ft)**

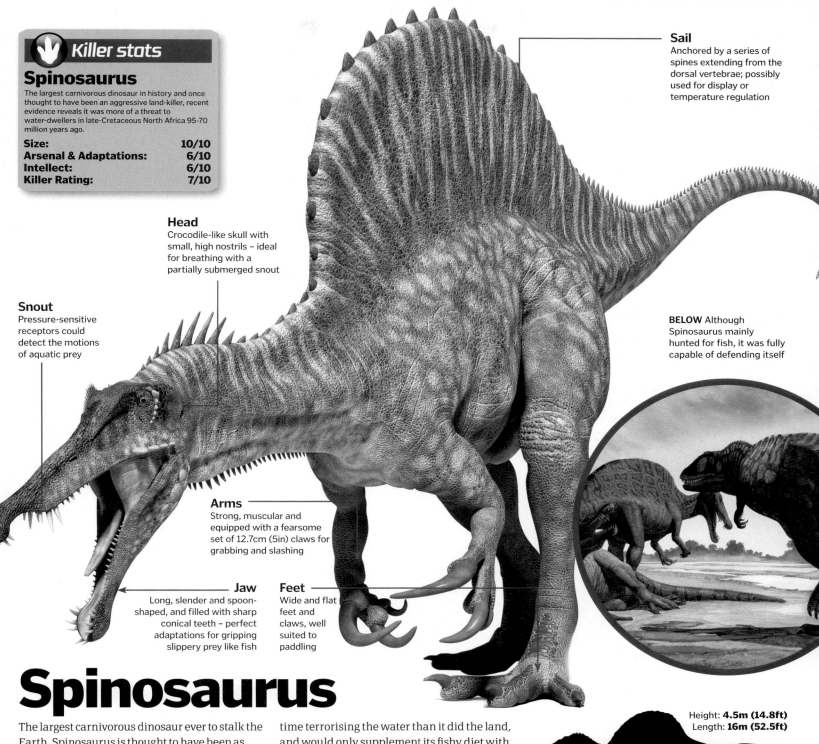

Killer stats

Spinosaurus

The largest carnivorous dinosaur in history and once thought to have been an aggressive land-killer, recent evidence reveals it was more of a threat to water-dwellers in late-Cretaceous North Africa 95-70 million years ago.

Size:	10/10
Arsenal & Adaptations:	6/10
Intellect:	6/10
Killer Rating:	7/10

Sail
Anchored by a series of spines extending from the dorsal vertebrae; possibly used for display or temperature regulation

Head
Crocodile-like skull with small, high nostrils – ideal for breathing with a partially submerged snout

Snout
Pressure-sensitive receptors could detect the motions of aquatic prey

BELOW Although Spinosaurus mainly hunted for fish, it was fully capable of defending itself

Arms
Strong, muscular and equipped with a fearsome set of 12.7cm (5in) claws for grabbing and slashing

Jaw
Long, slender and spoon-shaped, and filled with sharp conical teeth – perfect adaptations for gripping slippery prey like fish

Feet
Wide and flat feet and claws, well suited to paddling

Spinosaurus

The largest carnivorous dinosaur ever to stalk the Earth, Spinosaurus is thought to have been as long as one and a half double-decker London buses – 16 metres (52.5 feet) – and as heavy as a herd of Asian elephants (20 tonnes). Its vertebrae were 20 per cent larger than those of T-rex and to top it off, it sported a gigantic sail of skin supported by two-metre (6.6-foot)-long spines protruding from its back.

Despite its imposing physique, recent evidence suggests Spinosaurus spent more of its time terrorising the water than it did the land, and would only supplement its fishy diet with scavenged carrion. Its crocodile-like jaw had smooth, conical, pointed teeth, well adapted to spearing slippery prey like Onchopristis – eight-metre (26-foot)-long prehistoric sawfish – rather than ripping flesh from bone. Special structures in its snout helped it detect pressure waves caused by prey moving in the water.

Nevertheless, Spinosaurus was fast, strong and possessed a cruel set of claws, meaning it

Height: **4.5m (14.8ft)**
Length: **16m (52.5ft)**

could likely hold its own against other massive predators, like Carcharodontosaurus, who shared its territory. Despite what you might think, they never came up against the T-rex.

Carcharodontosaurus

Its name is a mouthful in more ways than one; Carcharodontosaurus ("Kar-KAR-o-don-toe-SORE-uss") means "shark-toothed lizard" and refers to the beast's jaw-full of 20-centimetre (eight-inch)-long serrated teeth. These could slice through flesh like switchblades through butter and leave enormous gaping wounds that would quickly incapacitate prey.

Although it was larger than T-rex and had an enormous skull the size of a person,

Carcharodontosaurus – along with its close cousins Giganotosaurus and Mapusaurus – was a more primitive dinosaur with a smaller brain. Instead, it had powerful legs and fossilised tracks suggest it was capable of outrunning T-rex – at about 32 kilometres (20 miles) per hour. Whether or not it actually did – given that its disproportionately small arms would be incapable of bracing its seven-tonne weight in a fall – is another matter.

Height: **4m (13.1ft)**
Length: **13m (42.7ft)**

Majungasaurus

Majungasaurus ("Mah-JUNG-a-SORE-uss") has a bit of a bad-lizard reputation; telltale tooth marks on Majungasaurus bones, found on its native island of Madagascar, line up perfectly with Majungasaurus's own dental patterns. That's right – the evidence suggests this one-tonne theropod feasted on its own kin, at least occasionally – surely the hallmark of a ruthless killer? What isn't known, though, is whether these were the spoils of active hunts or just efficient tidying up of already-dead relatives.

Height: **2m (6.6ft)**
Length: **6m (19.7ft)**

Height: **1.5m (4.9ft)**
Length: **3m (9.8ft)**

Deinonychus

The discovery of Deinonychus ("Dee-NON-i-KUSS") in 1964 overhauled our perception of dinosaurs as languid and lumbering; here was a creature clearly built for speedy pursuit. Almost twice the size of Velociraptor (insider tip – the 'Velociraptors' in Jurassic Park were actually modelled after the bigger, badder Deinonychus!), but a similar weight, it was a sprightly and most likely a quick-witted pack hunter. Among other advantages, it possessed interlocking vertebrae that allowed its tail to stiffen for balance when running, and a retractable 13-centimetre (five-inch) claw on each foot to disembowel prey restrained in its hands and jaw.

Giganotosaurus

Carcharodontosaurus's South American cousin, Giganotosaurus ("GIG-a-NOTE-o-SORE-uss") was another beast to rival T-rex for size. Depending on the specimen, it is thought to have been slightly smaller than Carcharodontosaurus, but longer, taller and more slender than T-rex. It was the fastest of the three, besting the others by at least 16 kilometres (ten miles) per hour, perhaps thanks to its superior balance.

It had a very large skull but, like Carcharodontosaurus, it was more neurologically primitive than T-rex; its brain was a puny half the size of T-rex's. Still, evidence suggests it had a keen sense of smell, which coupled with its athletic prowess and eight-tonne bulk made it a formidable foe.

Like Carcharodontosaurus, Giganotosaurus's teeth were serrated and laterally compressed – wide in profile but narrow when viewed from the front – making them ideal tools to deliver a series of injurious slices to the body of its prey, which would eventually keel over from exhaustion and blood loss.

Olfactory system
Large nostrils and advanced olfactory bulbs in its small brain gave it a keen sense of smell for hunting down prey

Bite
Although Giganotosaurus's jaw was only a third as powerful as T-rex's, it was packed with sharp, serrated 20cm (8in) daggers

Tail
Thin and pointed, it gave Giganotosaurus the ability make quick turns at top speeds without toppling over

Legs
Long and strong legs meant this killer could easily outsprint T-rex at an estimated 50kmh (31mph)

Height: **4m (13.1ft)**
Length: **12.5m (41ft)**

 Killer stats

Giganotosaurus

This giant razor-mouthed athlete roamed the swamplands of South America during the late-Cretaceous period, around 100-97 million years ago.

Size:	9/10
Arsenal & Adaptations:	9/10
Intellect:	2/10
Killer Rating:	9/10

© Corbis; Alamy; Science Photo Library

103

Dinosaurs' legacy

© Corbis

120 Ultimate T-rex facts

© SOL90

121 Could dinos fly?

© Nobu Tamura

123 Ceratosaurus

© Thinkstock

108
How are fossils made?

© Thinkstock

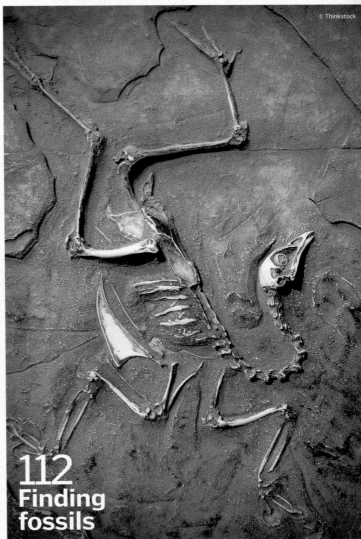

© Thinkstock

125
Cretaceous hunters

© Corbis

112
Finding fossils

© Getty Images

The extinction 106

Atmosphere
The volcanic eruptions added more carbon dioxide to the air, sucking the oxygen out of the water

The death of the dinosaurs

Loads of theories surround the death of the dinosaurs, we get to the bottom of it

It is believed that there have been at least five mass extinctions in the last 540 million years, the most famous being the one that signalled the end of the Cretaceous period around 65.5 million years ago and effectively wiped out the dinosaurs.

Palaeontologists initially believed that this mass extinction event was caused by climate and geological changes. This theory changed in the 1980s when scientists Luis and Walter Alvarez discovered a layer of iridium in the geological record that corresponds with the time that the dinosaurs became extinct. This substance existed only space and so its presence on Earth must have come as a result of

a comet, asteroid or meteor colliding with Earth. The discovery of the colossal Chicxulub Crater in Mexico's Yucatán Peninsula that dates back to the time of the mass extinction adds significant weight to this theory.

As a result, the Earth suffered a series of volcanic eruptions. Research has shown that the common factors in mass extinctions include large-scale lava flow and volcanic gases, which desecrate the land and suck all of the oxygen out of our oceans. The gases coughed out of volcanic eruptions, most notably carbon dioxide, are linked to short-term regional warming, acid rain and ozone depletion – the perfect cocktail to snuff out any creature

Based on the fossil record, mass extinctions are followed by recovery. Following the events of the Cretaceous period that rendered the dinosaurs extinct, the gradual recovery of vegetation was evident by the discovery of fern spores. Plants managed to adapt to cope with conditions on Earth. The fossil record tells us that the last dinosaur to walk the Earth was the Corythosaurus. This herbivore stood upright, with two arms used to strip and devour vegetation and was easily identifiable by a decorative semicircular crest on its head. Much effort has been spent searching for the causes of mass extinctions because ultimately there is no reason why another couldn't occur again.

Events of mass extinction

The mass extinction at the end of the Cretaceous period followed four others. The first signalled the end of the Ordovician period, which existed between 490-440 million years ago. The area to the north of the tropics was almost all ocean and the nature of the thriving marine faunas changed and the land saw the arrival of arthropods, such as Eodalmanitina, Cyclopyge and the Triarthrus. This mass extinction hit the flora and fauna, eroding much of the ecosystem of the most primitive creatures.

Next came the mass extinction at the end of the Devonian period (420-360 million years ago). This effectively wiped out around three-quarters of the Earth's species, though this could have taken the form of several extinctions over many millions of years rather than occurring as a result of a single event. The mass extinction at the end of the Permian period (300-250 million years go) wiped out 96 per cent of the Earth's species, meaning all that exists today is descended from the four per cent that remained. The penultimate mass extinction occurred at the Triassic-Jurassic period (250-140 million years ago), with climate change, flood basalts (that come as a result of a volcanic eruption coating the Earth with basalt lava) and asteroid impact all being possible causes.

Volcanic eruptions
Common factors in extinction events is the presence of lava and volcanic ash

The end of the dinosaurs is commonly disputed among scientists

Plant survival
After a mass extinction event, it is common for there to be recovery. After the dinosaurs became extinct, the plants, mostly ferns, .became the dominant survivor

Fauna
The Corythosaurus is theorised as being the last dinosaur standing after the mass-extinction event

"The common factors in mass extinctions include large-scale lava flow and volcanic gases"

What are fossils?

Obliterating the traditional perception of the origins and evolution of life on Earth, fossils grant us unique snapshots of what once lived on our ever-changing planet

Adpression

A form of fossilisation caused by compression within sedimentary rock. This type of fossilisation occurs mainly where fine sediment is deposited frequently, such as along rivers. Many fossilised plants are formed this way

Resin

Referred to as amber, fossil resin is a natural polymer excreted by trees and plants. As it is sticky and soft when produced, small invertebrates such as insects and spiders are often trapped and sealed within resin, preserving their form

Bioimmuration

Bioimmuration is a type of fossil that in its formation subsumes another organism, leaving an impression of it within the fossil. This type of fossilisation usually occurs between sessile skeletal organisms, such as oysters

© Michael S. Engel

© Slade Winstone

Types of fossilisation

Dependent on climate and ground conditions, deceased animals can be fossilised in many ways

Carbon dating

A crucial tool for palaeontologists, carbon dating allows ancient fossils to be accurately dated

Carbon dating is a method of radioactive dating used by palaeontologists that utilises the radioactive isotope carbon-14 to determine the time since it died and was fossilised. When an organism dies it stops replacing carbon-14, which is present in every carbonaceous organism on Earth, leaving the existing carbon-14 to decay. Carbon-14 has a half-life (the time it takes a decaying object to decrease in radioactivity by 50 per cent) of 5,730 years, so by measuring the decayed levels of carbon-14 in a fossil, its time of death can be extrapolated and its geological age determined.

This scientist is dating archaeological specimens in a Tandetron particle accelerator

© Science Photo Library

Permineralisation

A process in which mineral deposits form internal casts of organisms, permineralisation works when a deceased animal dies and then is rapidly submerged with groundwater. The water fills the creature's lungs and empty spaces, before draining away leaving a mineral cast

Recrystallisation

When a shelled creature's shell, bone or tissue maintains its original form but is replaced with a crystal – such as aragonite and calcite – then it is said to be recrystallised

Mold

A type of fossilisation process similar to permineralisation, molds occur when an animal is completely dissolved or destroyed, leaving only an organism-shaped hole in the rock. Molds can turn into casts if they are then filled with minerals

The origin of life on Earth is irrevocably trapped in deep time. The epic, fluid and countless beginnings, evolutions and extinctions are immeasurable to humankind; our chronology is fractured, the picture is incomplete. For while the diversity of life on Earth today is awe-inspiring, with animals living within the most extreme environments imaginable – environments we as humans brave every day in a effort to chart and understand where life begins and ends – it is but only a fraction of the total life Earth has seen inhabit it over geological time. Driven by the harsh realities of an ever-changing environment, Armageddon-level extinction events and the perpetual, ever-present force of natural selection, wondrous creatures with five eyes, fierce predators with 12-inch fangs and massive creatures twice the size of

a double-decker bus have long since ceased to exist. They are forgotten, buried by not just millions, but billions of years. Still, all is not lost to us. By exploiting Earth's natural processes and modern technology over the last two hundred years, scientists and palaeontologists have begun to

unravel Earth's tree of life and, through the discovery and excavation of fossils – preserved remains and traces of past life in Earth's crust – piece the jigsaw back together.

The fossilisation of an animal can occur in a variety of ways (see 'Types of fossilisation' boxout)

but, in general, it occurs when a recently deceased creature is rapidly buried by sediment or subsumed in an oxygen-deficient liquid. This has the effect of preserving parts of the creature – usually the harder, solid parts like its skeleton – often in the original, living form within the Earth's crust. The softer parts

"The softer parts of fossilised creatures tend not to survive due to the rapidity of decay"

of fossilised creatures tend not to survive due to the speed of decay and their replacement by minerals contained in their sediment or liquid casing, a process that can leave casings and impressions of the animal that once lived, but not its remains. Importantly, however, creature fossilisation tends to be specific to the environmental conditions in which it lived – and these in themselves are indicative of certain time periods in Earth's geological history. For example, certain species of trilobite (an extinct marine arthropod) are only found in certain rock strata (layers of sedimentary and igneous rocks formed through mineral deposition over millions of years), which itself is identifiable by its materials and mineralogic composition. This allows palaeontologists to extrapolate the environmental conditions (hot, cold, dry, wet, etc) that the animal lived and died in and, in partnership with radiometric dating, assign a date to the fossil and/or the period.

Interestingly, however, by studying the strata and the contained fossils over multiple layers, through a mixture of this form of palaeontology and phylogenetics (the study of evolutionary relatedness between organism groups), scientists can chart the evolution of animals over geological time scales. A good example of this process is the now known transition of certain species of dinosaur into birds. Here, by dating and analysing specimens such as archaeopteryx – a famous dinosaur/bird transition fossil – both by strata and by radiometric methods, as well as recording their molecular and morphological data, scientists can then chart its progress through strata layers to the present day. In addition, by following the fossil record in this way, palaeontologists can also attribute the geophysical/chemical changes to the rise, fall or transition of any one animal/plant group, reading the sediment's composition and structural data. For example, the Cretaceous-Tertiary extinction event is identified in sedimentary strata by a sharp decline in species' diversity – notably non-avian dinosaurs – and increased calcium deposits from dead plants and plankton.

Excavating any discovered fossil in order to date and analyse it is a challenging, time-consuming process, which requires special tools and equipment. These include picks and shovels, trowels, whisks, hammers, dental drills and even explosives. There is also an accepted academic method all professional palaeontologists follow when preparing, removing and transporting any discovered fossil. First, the fossil is partially freed from the sedimentary matrix it is encased in and labelled, photographed and reported. Next, the overlying rock (commonly referred to as the 'overburden') is removed using large tools up to a distance of two to three inches from the fossil, before it is once again photographed. Then, depending on the stability of the fossil, it is coated with a thin glue via brush or aerosol in order to strengthen its structure, before being wrapped in a series of paper, bubble wrap and Hessian cloth. Finally, it is transported to the laboratory.

The fossil record

By examining discovered fossils, it is possible to piece together a rough history of the development of life on Earth over a geological timescale

12 | CAMBRIAN | 542-488.3 Ma

The first geological period of the Paleozoic era, the Cambrian is unique in its high proportion of sedimentary layers and, consequently, adpression fossils. The Burgess Shale Formation, a notable fossil field dating from the Cambrian, has revealed many fossils including the genus opabinia, a five-eyed ocean crawler.

11 | ORDOVICIAN | 488.3-443.7 Ma

Boasting the highest sea levels on the Palaezoic era, the Ordovician saw the proliferation of planktonics, brachiopods and cephalopods. Nautiloids, suspension feeders, are among the largest creatures from this period to be discovered.

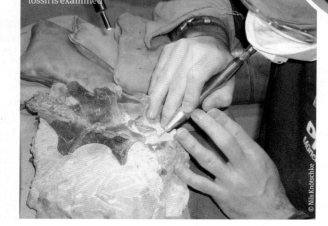

A Europasaurus fossil is examined

10 | SILURIAN | 443.7-416 Ma

With its base set at major extinction event at the end of the Ordovician, the silurian fossils found differ markedly from those that pre-date the period. Notable life developments include the first bony fish, and organisms with moveable jaws.

9 | DEVONIAN | 416-359.2 Ma

An incredibly important time for the development of life, the Devonian period has relinquished fossils demonstrating the evolution of the pectoral and pelvic fins of fish into legs. The first land-based creatures, tetrapods and arthopods, become entrenched and seed-bearing plants spread across dry lands. A notable Devonian find is the genus tiktaalik.

3 | PALEOGENE | 65.5-23.03 Ma

The first period of the Cenozoic era, the Paleogene is notable for the rise of mammals as the dominant animal group on Earth, driven by the Cretaceous-Tertiary extinction event that wiped out the dinosaurs. The most important fossil to be discovered from this period is Darwinius, a lemur-like creature uncovered from a shale quarry in Messel, Germany.

4 | CRETACEOUS | 145.5-65.5 Ma

Fossils discovered from the Cretaceous indicate an explosion of insect diversification, with the first ants and grasshoppers evolving, as well as the dominance of large dinosaurs such as the colossal Tyrannosaurus rex. Mammals increased in diversity, however remained small and largely marsupial.

5 | JURASSIC | 199.6-145.5 Ma

The period in Earth's history when the supercontinent Pangaea broke up in to the northern Laurasia and southern Gondwana, the Jurassic saw an explosion in marine and terrestrial life. The fossil record points to dinosaurs thriving, such as Megalosaurus, an increase in large predatory fish like Ichthyosaurus, as well as the evolution of the first birds – shown famously by the Archaeopteryx fossil find.

7 | PERMIAN | 299-251 Ma

A period characterised by the diversification of early amniotes (egg-bearing invertebrates) in to mammals, turtles, lepidosaurs and archosaurs, the Permian has yielded many diverse fossils. Notable examples include reptile therapsids, dragonflies and, driven by late warmer climates, lycopod trees.

8 | CARBONIFEROUS | 359.2-299 Ma

A period of significant glaciation, the Carboniferous saw the development of ferns and conifers, bivalve molluscs and a wide-variety of basal tetrapods such as labyrinthodontia. Notable fossilised finds include the seed ferns pecopteris and neuropteris.

2 | NEOGENE | 23.03-2.588 Ma

Covering 23 million years, the Neogene period's fossils show a marked development in mammals and birds, with many hominin remains excavated. The extinct hominid australopithecus afarensis – a common ancestor of the genus homo (that of modern humans) – is one of the most notable fossil finds, as exemplified in the specimens Lucy and Selam.

1 | QUATERNARY | 2.588-0.00 Ma

The most recent period in Earth's history, the Quaternary is characterised by major changes in climate, as well as the evolution and dispersement of modern humans. Due to the rapid changes in environment and climate (ie, ice ages), many larger mammal fossils have been discovered, including those of mammoths and sabre-toothed cats.

6 | TRIASSIC | 250-200 Ma

Beginning and ending with an extinction event, the Triassic period's fossils show the evolution of the first dinosaurs such as Coelophysis, a small carnivorous biped animal. Fossil evidence also shows the development of modern corals and reefs.

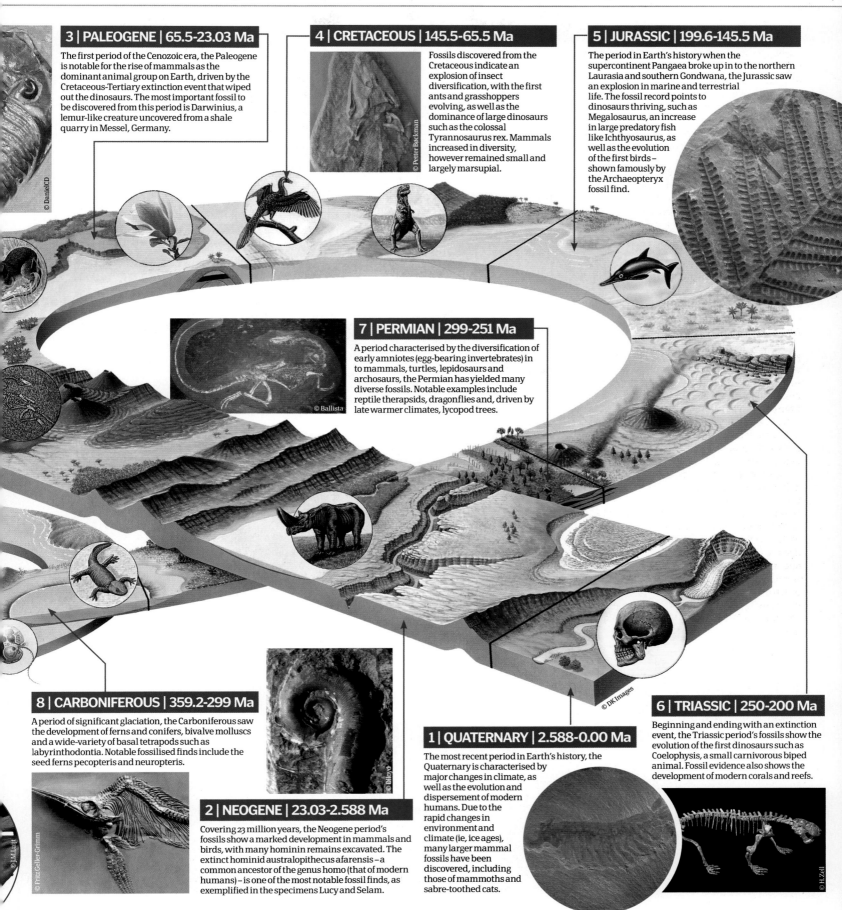

© DanielCD
© Petter Bøckman
© Ballista
© I.M.Lujit
© Fritz Geller-Grimm
© Bibaycb
© DK Images
© H.Zell

Finding fossils

How are prehistoric remains uncovered and what can scientists learn from them? Let us dig up the facts…

Ever since Mary Anning first began piecing together the fossils of Jurassic beasts in the early nineteenth century, scientists have been learning more and more about the dinosaurs that ruled the world millions of years ago. Buried deep beneath the ground for aeons, the remains of countless extinct creatures are waiting to be unearthed by palaeontologists, who can gradually unlock their secrets.

Dinosaurs and other prehistoric fossils have been discovered around the world for thousands of years, with reports of 'dragon bones' found in China more likely indicating some of the earliest dino finds. However, it wasn't until the brilliant scientists of the Enlightenment in the late-18th and early-19th centuries that it became clear just how old these ancient skeletons really were. Before long, fossil hunting became an obsession for naturalists and amateurs alike, with the strange extinct 'lizards' being discovered at sites all over the globe.

Though ground-penetrating radar now helps archaeologists identify hidden underground remains, modern palaeontologists still often rely on the same methods their 19th-century predecessors did: plain luck. Of course, through a greater understanding of geology, as well as by searching in so-called fossil hotspots, it's possible to predict where fossils will likely be found. Once a fossil site has been identified, the long and delicate process of unearthing the dino remains begins.

Digging for fossils can be as simple as sieving through sand and silt in the search for tiny teeth, or cracking open large rocks with a hammer and chisel to see what may be lying within. Hills, quarries, mountainsides and ravines are often prime locations for fossil finds, as the deep layers of rock have become exposed by millions of years of erosion. In these cases heavy diggers and drills are crucial to reach the finds. Dozens of scientists, students and even enthusiastic volunteers are employed with brushes and trowels during the course of an excavation. However, because of the delicate nature of specimens that are millions of years old, it can often take what must seem like another million to safely uproot an entire dinosaur skeleton.

Of course, palaeontologists do much more than just dig up old bones. Mixing together the disciplines of geology and biology, palaeontology is the study of fossils to reveal the history of life on Earth. So, once the fossilised remains have been fully excavated, the real work can begin back in the lab. Here scientists painstakingly remove any residual earth and stone from the specimens in preparation for full analysis. Electron microscopes, CAT scanners and X-ray machines are all employed to gather as much information about the creature as possible.

By studying the shape, length and arrangement of each fossilised bone, palaeontologists have been able to determine not only what certain dinosaurs looked like and how they moved, but also what they ate. The discovery of indentations on fossilised arm bones similar to those found on modern birds has also indicated that many species of dinosaur were actually feathered.

Bigger, stranger and ever-more unbelievable dino discoveries are being made all the time, each one challenging past theories and shedding new light on the distant land of the Mesozoic beasts. Thanks to the pioneering work of the scientists and enthusiasts of the past, each new fossil found could slot yet another piece of the prehistoric jigsaw into place.

How fossils form

How do the remains of prehistoric animals become fossils, and why do they survive through the ages?

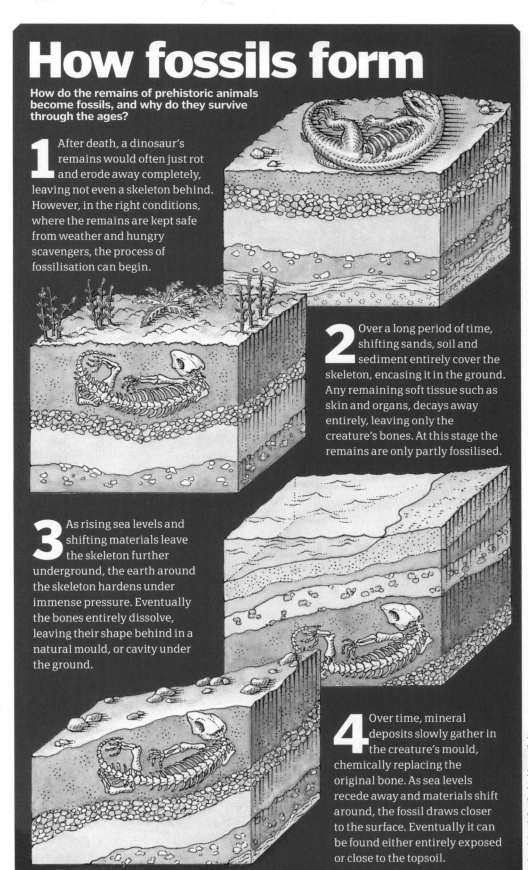

1 After death, a dinosaur's remains would often just rot and erode away completely, leaving not even a skeleton behind. However, in the right conditions, where the remains are kept safe from weather and hungry scavengers, the process of fossilisation can begin.

2 Over a long period of time, shifting sands, soil and sediment entirely cover the skeleton, encasing it in the ground. Any remaining soft tissue such as skin and organs, decays away entirely, leaving only the creature's bones. At this stage the remains are only partly fossilised.

3 As rising sea levels and shifting materials leave the skeleton further underground, the earth around the skeleton hardens under immense pressure. Eventually the bones entirely dissolve, leaving their shape behind in a natural mould, or cavity under the ground.

4 Over time, mineral deposits slowly gather in the creature's mould, chemically replacing the original bone. As sea levels recede away and materials shift around, the fossil draws closer to the surface. Eventually it can be found either entirely exposed or close to the topsoil.

Digging for dinosaurs

How palaeontologists discover and unearth prehistoric giants

Bulldozers, hammers, chisels, drills and even dynamite – you'd be forgiven for thinking these were part of a construction-site inventory. In fact, they are the basic tools a palaeontologist will use to uncover the mysteries of the past. From removing tons of topsoil with diggers and other heavy machinery, to carefully clearing away clinging dust and debris with delicate brushes, the process of excavating a dinosaur skeleton can take many years.

The largest dino fossil

Even in this ancient time when giants ruled the Earth, sky and sea, Dreadnoughtus schrani truly was a behemoth of a creature. Standing over two-storeys tall and weighing as much 60 tonnes, the remains of this beast were found by a team in Patagonia, Argentina, and have been dated back over 77 million years. A member of the titanosaur sauropod group of dinosaurs, Dreadnoughtus was a plant-eater and is to date the largest known land animal ever to have lived.

Two Dreadnoughtus titanosaurs were found at the site, and it's believed the pair died in a massive flash flood, which would explain why their remains were so complete. The preservation of the skeletons enabled scientists to take full advantage of 3D-printing technology, scanning in each individual bone into a digital format for even greater scrutiny. This 3D rendering of Dreadnoughtus provided even greater insight into how it likely looked and moved.

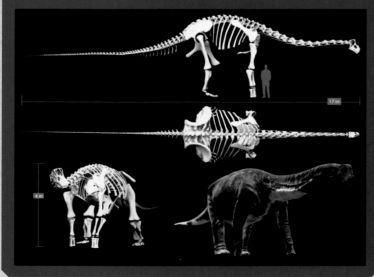

17 m

4 m

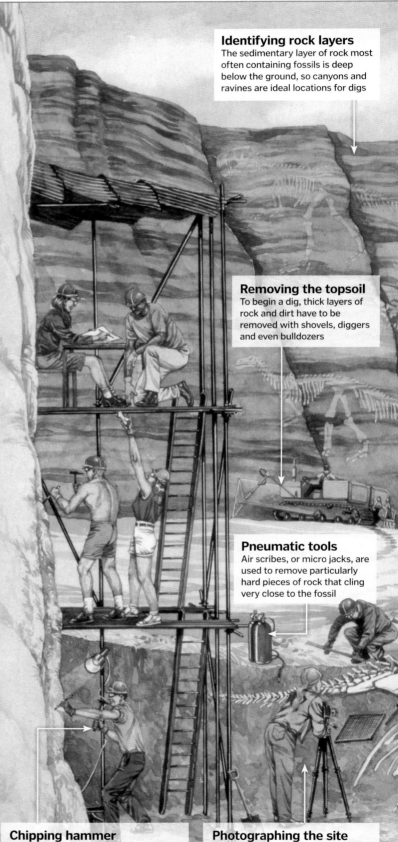

Identifying rock layers
The sedimentary layer of rock most often containing fossils is deep below the ground, so canyons and ravines are ideal locations for digs

Removing the topsoil
To begin a dig, thick layers of rock and dirt have to be removed with shovels, diggers and even bulldozers

Pneumatic tools
Air scribes, or micro jacks, are used to remove particularly hard pieces of rock that cling very close to the fossil

Chipping hammer
When searching in areas where fossils have already been discovered, simply chipping away and analysing hard stone could unearth a new find

Photographing the site
Images of the site can help palaeontologists piece together what the landscape would have looked like when the creature was alive

Studying the surroundings
Dig-team members have to carefully record the arrangement and surroundings of the fossil, to learn as much as they can about how the creature lived and died

Moving to the lab
Once they are carefully recorded and stored, the fossils are transported off the site for closer analysis

Protecting the bones
Before being removed, each bone is wrapped in paper towels, and then encased in plaster strips that dry to protect the fossils

Isolating the fossil
After the main layers of dirt are cleared, the fossil is carefully dusted to isolate it from the surrounding earth

Tools of the trade
What do you need for a fossil dig?

Chisels
Chisel blades come in a range of sizes for either cracking apart larger stone or trimming away a rock face

Hammers
Crack and chipping hammers are essential for carefully removing and trimming hard rock. They are also needed for working with chisels

Sieve
Not all fossils come in huge sizes, so wire sieves are perfect for sifting through sand and silt for teeth and other small remains

Maps
If travelling to more remote locations, as well as for making reliable notes for future reference, a good map and compass are a must

Brushes
Small, soft bristles are ideal for working with delicate remains, while larger, harder brushes are best for removing thicker dust

Journals and reference
Accurately recording everything you find, where it's found, as well as referencing what it could be, is vital for making new discoveries

© Getty; Rodolfo Nogueira/Stocktrek Images/Corbis; DK Images

ON THE MAP

The world's fossil hotspots
1 Jurassic Coast, Devon and Dorset, UK
2 Auca Mahuevo, Patagonia, Argentina
3 Dinosaur Cove, Victoria, Australia
4 Joggins Fossil Cliffs, Nova Scotia, Canada
5 Chengjiang Fossil Site, Chenjiang County, China
6 Como Bluff, Wyoming, USA

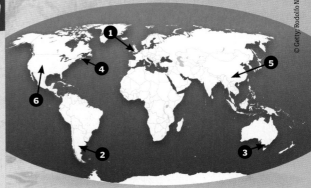

01 **The word 'dinosaur' means terrible lizard**
The word 'dinosaur' was first used in 1841 by biologist Sir Richard Owen. It is from the Greek word 'deinos', meaning terrible or great, and 'sauros', meaning lizard.

Camarasaurus
Late Jurassic
North America

02 **Dinosaurs were not lizards**
Despite being named 'terrible lizards', dinosaurs were anatomically very different from other reptiles and are not that closely related.

Monolophosaurus
Mid Jurassic
China

FACT 3
200 TONS
No dinosaur even came close to the weight of a blue whale

101
GIGANTIC FACTS ABOUT
DINOSAURS
WE'VE DUG UP THE MOST ESSENTIAL DINOSAUR FACTS THAT EVERYONE SHOULD KNOW

Deinonychus
Early Cretaceous
North America

Sauropelta
Early Cretaceous
North America

04 **Cavemen never met the dinosaurs**
The reign of the dinosaurs came to an end 66 million years ago, but humans have only been around for 200,000 years. Our ancestors did not share a world with the dinosaurs, but they did encounter sabre-toothed cats and woolly mammoths.

Corythosaurus
Late Cretaceous
North America

05 No one knows what colour dinosaurs really were

The coloured pictures of dinosaurs seen in textbooks are guesswork based on what we know about animals today, but scientists have analysed melanosomes (pigment cells) found in fossils and are piecing together their real colours.

"230 million years ago, the Earth was dominated by mammal-like reptiles, such as Dimetrodon and Lystrosaurus"

Stegosaurus
Late Jurassic
North America

FACT 6

5cm
Stegosaurus had a brain the size of a plum

Triceratops
Late Cretaceous
North America

07 Triceratops had up to 800 teeth

Triceratops might be known for their horns, but these icons of the Cretaceous period had another special feature. They had hundreds of teeth, stacked on top of one another in groups of three to five in piles called 'dental batteries'.

Dimetrodon
Early Permian
North America

© Corbis; Alamy; Thinkstock

08 Not all prehistoric reptiles were dinosaurs

Over 230 million years ago, the Earth was dominated by large mammal-like reptiles like Dimetrodon and Lystrosaurus. They might look like dinosaurs, but they are actually more closely related to modern mammals than they are to dinosaurs.

FACT 9

3.5kg
Compsognathus, one of the smallest dinos, was only just larger than a chicken

Compsognathus
Late Jurassic
Europe

Sauropods

These long-necked giants are among the largest animals to have ever lived

10 Sauropods were huge herbivores

The four-legged dinosaurs with long tails and necks are known as sauropods. The most common were Diplodocus and Camarasaurus.

11 Diplodocus had 15 vertebrae in its neck

At least, we think it did – there are very few complete specimens. For comparison, a human has seven neck vertebrae.

12 Sauropods did not live in water

Early ideas about how sauropods like Diplodocus lived portrayed them walking underwater like hippos. They had nostrils on the top of their heads, and scientists thought they would use their necks like snorkels. However, with large bodies, the crushing weight of water would have prevented them from breathing, and we now know they lived on land.

13 Titanosaurs laid the largest eggs

The larger an egg is, the thicker its shell has to be. Even the monstrous titanosaurs had to lay relatively small eggs so that oxygen and carbon dioxide could cross over the walls of the shell.

FACT 14

33m

Diplodocus was the length of three buses

Aegyptosaurus
Mid Cretaceous
Africa

15 You can tell if a dinosaur was female by looking at her bones

Medullary bone lines the inside of bones and stores calcium to make eggshells. It forms in female birds, its presence in fossils can also reveal the sex.

Pachycephalosaurus
Late Cretaceous
North America

Charonosaurus
Late Cretaceous
China

Struthiomimus
Late Cretaceous
North America

22 Hadrosaurs had duck-like bills

Hadrosaurs were the first dinosaurs found in North America, and since the nineteenth century, hundreds have been unearthed. These herbivores had a very distinctive appearance, with duck-like beaks adapted for clipping vegetation, and crested heads that might have helped to transmit sounds over long distances.

23 Ornithomimids looked and lived like ostriches

Ornithomimid means 'bird mimic', and these two-legged dinosaurs really do look familiar. They had long, muscular legs, large, rounded bodies and long necks with small heads. Like modern ostriches, these dinosaurs were extremely fast on their feet.

24 Dinosaurs didn't have two brains

Stegosaurus had a tiny brain, but at the base of its spine there was an enlarged space. Scientists once thought it might have housed a second, larger brain to control its legs, but this idea has been discredited as birds have a similar opening to store the energy-rich substance glycogen.

25 Pachcephalosaurs had thick skulls

Pachycephalosaur means 'thick-headed lizard'. The bone at the top of their skull could be up to 25cm (10in) thick, and their faces were covered in bumps and spikes. These dramatic features could have been for fighting, or they might just have been for show, like the antlers on modern deer.

16 Ankylosaurus was one of the last surviving dinosaurs
These heavily armoured dinosaurs had clubbed tails, weighed over 4,000kg (8,818lb) and were covered in bony plates. They were extremely tough, and no predator could tackle a full-grown adult.

17 Herds of dinosaurs were fossilised together
At a bonebed in Alberta, Canada, at least 27 ceratopsids with frilled heads and horns were found buried together.

FACT 18
18.5m
Sauroposeidon was about three times taller than a giraffe

19 Pterosaurs weren't dinosaurs
Pterodactyls are the iconic flying dinosaurs, but they weren't actually dinosaurs at all. Dinosaurs were all land animals. Quetzalcoatlus, the largest pterosaur of all, had a 12m (39ft) wingspan, making it the largest animal that ever flew.

20 Big bodies kept dinosaurs warm
This process is known as 'thermal inertia'. The larger the body of an animal, the lower the surface-to-volume ratio – preventing heat escaping from the skin.

21 The Sea level dropped as the dinosaurs went extinct
At around the time the dinosaurs went extinct, the sea level fell by 150m (492ft).

Styracosaurus
Late Cretaceous
Canada

Sinornithosaurus
Early Cretaceous
China

26 Dinosaurs had feathers
Despite what you might see in textbooks, museums and even in this bookazine, we now know that most dinosaurs were not all scaly and bald. We have known for a while that the two-legged theropods had feathers, but in 2014 a very distantly related beaked dinosaur found in Siberia was also found to have feathers, suggesting scales were replaced early in dinosaur evolution.

27 Ceratopsians had horned faces
The most famous ceratopsian is Triceratops, but there were other dinosaurs with horns and frills. These huge herbivores started to appear around 160 million years ago, and it is thought the frill was used as protection against predators, to impress potential mates and as a radiator to get rid of excess heat.

Nests & eggs

28 All dinosaurs laid eggs
Dinosaurs all reproduced by laying eggs like modern-day birds, and some of the hatchlings were thousands of times smaller than the full-grown adults.

29 Some dinosaurs cared for their young
Adult Psittacosaurus have been found alongside the fossilised remains of their young, and the bones of older babies have been found in the nests of Maiasaura, indicating that they probably helped to raise their young.

30 The largest dinosaur egg was over 60cm long
The largest dinosaur eggs were found in Mongolia in the 1990s, and measured around 45cm (17.7ft) across. Compared to the size of the adults, they are still surprisingly small.

31 Some of the best dinosaur fossils are babies
A 113-million-year-old fossilised baby dinosaur found in Italy still contains traces of preserved soft tissue, including intestines and tail muscles.

32 Baby dinosaurs grew rapidly
Sauropods like Diplodocus weighed a tiny 5kg (11lb) at birth, and grew to 10,000 times their size within just 30 years. Fossilised embryos show sauropod bones filled with blood vessels, bringing nutrients to allow rapid growth.

33 There are two main types of dinosaur egg
Dinosaur eggs can be divided into two main categories – spheroidal and elongated. Rounder eggs were laid by herbivores such as sauropods, while elongated, bird-like eggs were laid by theropods.

34 Oviraptors didn't steal eggs
The name 'Oviraptor' means egg thief, but these dinosaurs weren't criminals. They were actually devoted parents, and fossilised nests found in Mongolia show they arranged their eggs in spiral layers.

Tyrannosaurus rex

35 You probably couldn't outrun a Tyrannosaurus

Computer simulations of T-rex running suggest that it had a top speed of around 29kmh (18mph). Not quite fast enough to catch up with a car, like in Jurassic Park, but quick enough to catch any human that's not an athlete.

Head
It measured 1.5m (4.9ft) long, and had eye and nose cavities. The skull was of thick and heavy bone, although in some points it was pretty flexible.

36 The largest T-rex fossil is called Sue

Complete dinosaur fossils are incredibly rare, but there is one T-rex specimen that stands out from the rest. Sue is over 12.8m (40ft) long and stands over 3.9m (13ft) high. She is on display at the Chicago Field Museum and is the most complete specimen ever recovered.

37 Stegosaurus never met Tyrannosaurus

Despite being depicted together, these two would never have been in the same place at the same time. Stegosaurus lived during the Jurassic period and went extinct around 80 million years before T-rex first appeared at the end of the Cretaceous period.

Among the T-rex's favourite prey were the Ceratopsians, such as Triceratops

38 Some dinosaurs had a wishbone

The 'V'-shaped wishbone you find in your Sunday roast is also present in meat-eating theropods such as T-rex.

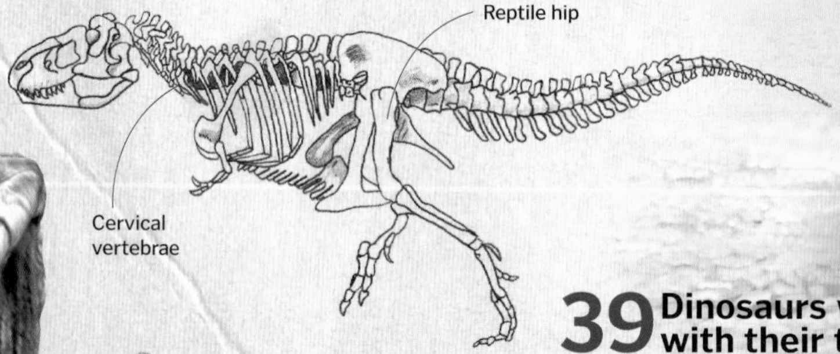

Reptile hip

Cervical vertebrae

39 Dinosaurs walked with their tails up

Dinosaurs like T-rex had enormous heads, and used their tails as a counterweight, holding them up for balance.

40 The meat-eating dinosaurs were all theropods

T-rex, Allosaurus and Deinonychus belonged to a group of dinosaurs known as theropods. Some members of this group are the largest carnivores ever to have walked the Earth.

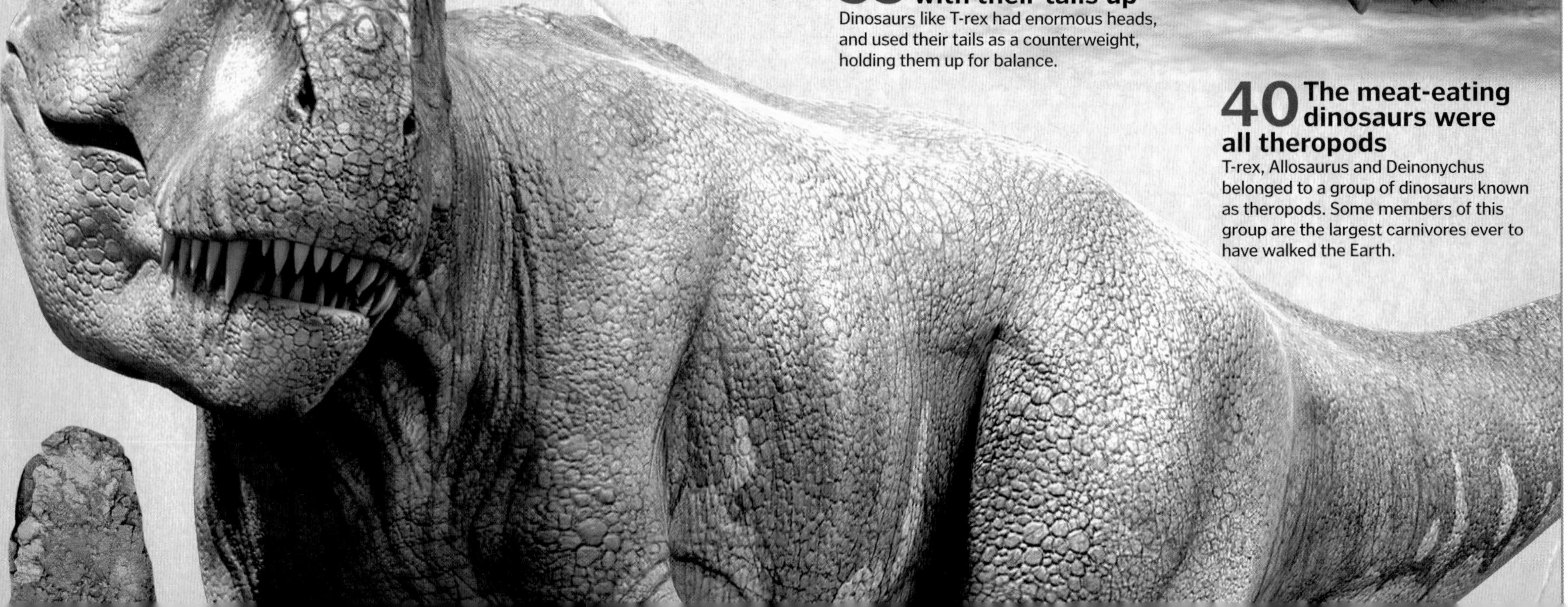

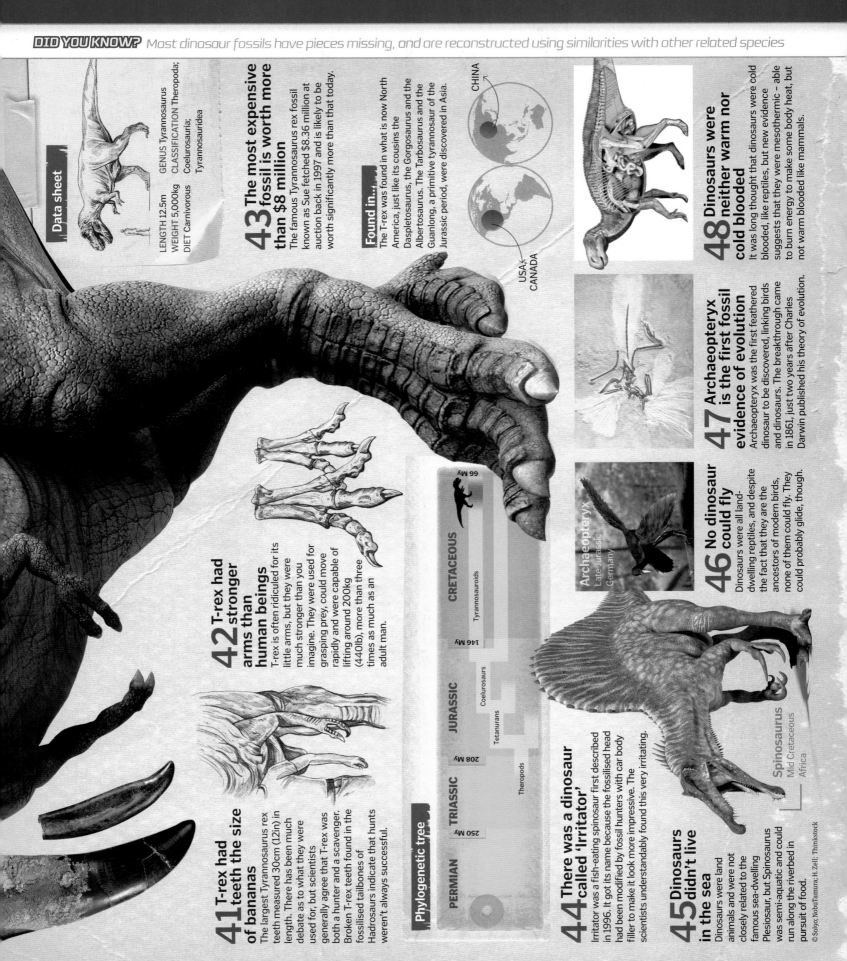

Data sheet

GENUS Tyrannosaurus
CLASSIFICATION Theropoda;
Coelurosauria;
Tyrannosauridea

LENGTH 12.5m
WEIGHT 5,000kg
DIET Carnivorous

43 The most expensive fossil is worth more than $8 million

The famous Tyrannosaurus rex fossil known as Sue fetched $8.36 million at auction back in 1997 and is likely to be worth significantly more than that today.

Found in...

The T-rex was found in what is now North America, just like its cousins the Daspletosaurus, the Gorgosaurus and the Albertosaurus. The Tarbosaurus and the Guanlong, a primitive tyrannosaur of the Jurassic period, were discovered in Asia.

CHINA

USA; CANADA

48 Dinosaurs were neither warm nor cold blooded

It was long thought that dinosaurs were cold blooded, like reptiles, but new evidence suggests that they were mesothermic – able to burn energy to make some body heat, but not warm blooded like mammals.

41 T-rex had teeth the size of bananas

The largest Tyrannosaurus rex teeth measured 30cm (12in) in length. There has been much debate as to what they were used for, but scientists generally agree that T-rex was both a hunter and a scavenger. Broken T-rex teeth found in the fossilised tailbones of Hadrosaurs indicate that hunts weren't always successful.

42 T-rex had stronger arms than human beings

T-rex is often ridiculed for its little arms, but they were much stronger than you imagine. They were used for grasping prey, could move rapidly and were capable of lifting around 200kg (440lb), more than three times as much as an adult man.

Phylogenetic tree

PERMIAN	TRIASSIC	JURASSIC	CRETACEOUS
250 My	208 My	146 My	66 My

Theropods
Tetanurans
Coelurosaurs
Tyrannosauroids

44 There was a dinosaur called 'Irritator'

Irritator was a fish-eating spinosaur first described in 1996. It got its name because the fossilised head had been modified by fossil hunters with car body filler to make it look more impressive. The scientists understandably found this very irritating.

45 Dinosaurs didn't live in the sea

Dinosaurs were land animals and were not closely related to the famous sea-dwelling Plesiosaur, but Spinosaurus was semi-aquatic and could run along the riverbed in pursuit of food.

Spinosaurus
Mid Cretaceous
Africa

46 No dinosaur could fly

Dinosaurs were all land-dwelling reptiles, and despite the fact that they are the ancestors of modern birds, none of them could fly. They could probably glide, though.

Archaeopteryx
Late Jurassic
Germany

47 Archaeopteryx is the first fossil evidence of evolution

Archaeopteryx was the first feathered dinosaur to be discovered, linking birds and dinosaurs. The breakthrough came in 1861, just two years after Charles Darwin published his theory of evolution.

© Solpo; NobuTamura; H.Zell; Thinkstock

Classification
Dinosaurs can be split into two major groups, with many more subdivisions

49 **The meat-eating dinosaurs walked on two feet**
All the carnivorous dinosaurs were theropods (although not all theropods were carnivores) and walked upright on their two hind legs. They typically had hollow bones, three main fingers on each hand and foot, and sharp, curved teeth and claws used for hunting and eating.

50 **Dinosaurs either had lizard hips or bird hips**
Dinosaurs can be divided into two major groups based on their hipbones. The Ornithischia, or 'bird-hipped' dinosaurs had a pubic bone that pointed toward the tail, and the Saurischia, 'lizard-hipped' dinosaurs pointed toward the head. Interestingly, birds evolved from lizard-hipped dinosaurs.

51 **Most dinosaurs ate plants**
Dinosaurs are often portrayed as fearsome hunters, but the majority of species were herbivores. Even some of the ferocious-looking theropods actually ate plants and used their sharp claws for digging.

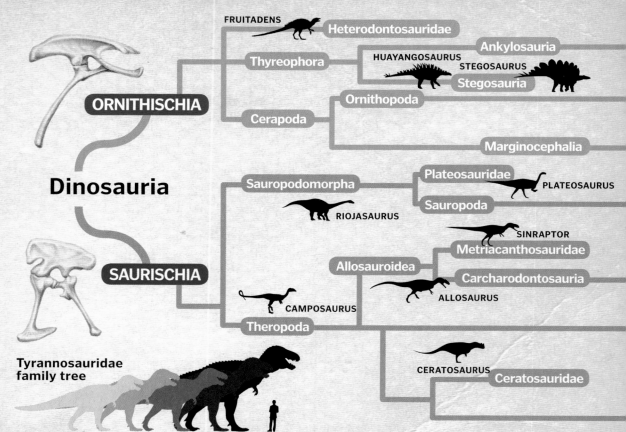

Tyrannosauridae family tree

Gorgosaurus ■ Daspletosaurus ■ Albertosaurus ■ Tarbosaurus ■ Tyrannosaurus

56 **Dinosaurs lived during the Mesozoic Era**
Dinosaurs ruled the Earth for 165 million years, in a time period known as the Mesozoic Era. This era can be split into three periods, Triassic, Jurassic and Cretaceous

57 **Dinosaurs first appeared 230 million years ago**
Dinosaurs evolved during the Triassic period, between 250 and 200 million years ago. The warm, dry conditions were perfect for breeding reptiles.

58 **Volcanic eruptions contributed to the extinction of the dinosaurs**
Huge lava flows are present in the fossil record for about 500,000 years before the extinction of the dinosaurs, and many scientists think eruptions contributed to their extinction by filling the air with a thick cloud of ash.

59 **Early dinosaurs lived on the continent of Pangaea**
When dinosaurs first appeared, the landmasses of the Earth were joined into a supercontinent called Pangaea. This later fractured into two continents – Laurasia and Gondwana.

Camposaurus — Late Triassic, North America
Riojasaurus — Late Triassic, South America
Apatosaurus — Late Jurassic, North America
Torvosaurus — Late Jurassic, North America, Europe
Stegosaurus — Late Jurassic, North America, Europe

TRIASSIC 252–201 MILLION YEARS AGO
JURASSIC 201–145 MILLION YEARS AGO

52 There were more than 700 species of dinosaur

To date, over 700 species of dinosaur have been identified, but only around 300 have been confirmed as entirely unique. There are more yet to be found, so this number will continue to change.

53 There are hundreds of dinosaurs yet to be found

It is estimated that we have only found around a tenth of the dinosaur species that ever existed. Some are buried in rocks we cannot reach, while others lived in areas where conditions did not favour fossil formation.

54 There were fewer dinosaur species than we thought

Hundreds of species of dinosaur have been named, but few baby dinosaurs have been found. Scientists have reviewed the evidence and have found that some smaller species might actually be the babies of larger species.

MINMI

HYPSILOPHODON

Hypsilophodontidae

EUOPLOCEPHALUS ANKYLOSAURUS

Iguanodontia

CHARONOSAURUS IGUANODON

DRACOREX PACHYCEPHALOSAURUS

Pachycephalosauria

CENTROSAURUS

Ceratopsia

PROTOCERATOPS TRICERATOPS

Diplodocoidea

BRACHIOSAURUS

Neosauropoda

DIPLODOCUS

Brachiosauridae

CARCHARODONTOSAURUS

Titanosauria

ARGENTINOSAURUS

GIGANOTOSAURUS MAPUSAURUS

THERIZINOSAURUS

SHUVUUIA

Spinosauridae

Ornithomimosauria

Therizinosauria

Alvarezsauridae

SPINOSAURUS

OVIRAPTOR

Oviraptorosauria

TROODON

Birds

VELOCIRAPTOR

Troodontidae

Dromaeosauridae

UTAHRAPTOR

Tryannosauroidea

Abelisauroidae

RAJASAURUS

MAJUNGASAURUS

TARBOSAURUS

TYRANNOSAURUS

Ceratosaurus
Late Jurassic
North America,
Europe

55 Dinosaurs are still alive today

In the 19th century the fossilised remains of a feathered dinosaur called Archaeopteryx were discovered, and since then evidence linking dinosaurs to birds has stacked up. It is thought that early birds started to evolve from the carnivorous theropods in the late Jurassic, and a few managed to survive the mass extinction, giving rise to the bird species we see today.

© Thinkstock; Science Photo Library

60 Sea levels were at an all-time high in the Cretaceous

During the Cretaceous period, sea levels rose and fell dramatically, and large areas of land disappeared under water. At times the sea was 100-250m (330-820ft) higher than it is today.

61 High oxygen levels fuelled fires during the extinction event

During the Cretaceous period, oxygen levels in the atmosphere were much higher than they are now, which may have helped to fuel fires after the famous meteor impact 66 million years ago, contributing to the mass extinction.

62 They experienced more than one mass extinction

There was a mass extinction at the end of the Triassic period, when many land animals died out, leaving room for the evolution of some of the giants of the dinosaur world.

Triceratops
Late Cretaceous
North America

Tarbosaurus
Late Cretaceous
Asia

Euoplocephalus
Late Cretaceous
North America

Utahraptor
Early Cretaceous
North America

Peter Scott / Art Agenency

CRETACEOUS 145–66 MILLION YEARS AGO

Minmi
Early Cretaceous
Australia

63 Armoured dinosaurs are known as 'Thyreophora'

Stegosaurus and Ankylosaurus are famous for their armour plating and were members of a group of dinosaurs called Thyreophora. Anklosauria were the most heavily armoured and had bony plates, spikes and clubbed tails.

64 Dinosaur's legs are positioned beneath their bodies

Crocodiles and lizards walk with their legs out to the sides, but dinosaurs have their legs underneath their bodies, allowing them to run faster.

65 Some dinosaurs swallowed rocks

Many plant-eating dinosaurs have been found with groups of rounded stones inside their ribcages, indicating they swallowed stones to aid digestion, like modern birds.

66 Some dinosaurs had a mixture of dinosaur-like and bird-like features

Birds are descended from small theropods. They walked upright on two legs and fossil evidence shows that some of them had feathers.

Caudipteryx
Early Cretaceous
Asia

67 Dinosaurs lived in a changing world

Around 250 million years ago, all of Earth's landmasses were joined in a supercontinent known as Pangaea. During the reign of the dinosaurs, this landmass split apart, first into two and then into the seven continents we see today.

68 Paleontologists study fossils

Scientists that study dinosaur remains are known as palaeontologists. Anthropologists study human remains, and archaeologists study artefacts.

69 Some herbivores had self-sharpening teeth

As their jaws closed, the teeth of some plant-eating dinosaurs would grind against each other, wearing the surface into a sharp point.

70 Hadrosaurs had the most teeth

The duck-billed dinosaurs had up to 50 rows of teeth stacked on top of one another, making a total of over 1,000.

Rajasaurus
Late Cretaceous
India

TITANOSAURUS
Late Cretaceous
Asia

76 The longest dinosaur name has 23 letters

Micropachycephalosaurus means 'tiny thick-headed lizard'. It might have the longest name, but it was only about 1m (3.3ft) long.

DID YOU KNOW? *In 2005, collagen tissue was found in a T-rex fossil. Scientists think iron molecules helped prevent its decay*

71 Dinosaurs had giant fleas

Fossilised remains reveal that dinosaurs in the Cretaceous and Jurassic were hosts to giant flea-like insects measuring ten times the size of modern fleas.

72 Ornithopods walked on two legs

Dinosaurs like Iguanodon and the duck-billed Hadrosaurs walked upright on two legs, and lived in herds like modern-day antelope.

73 one dinosaur is named after the Harry Potter books

Dracorex hogwartsia ("dragon king of Hogwarts") was a pachycephalosaur with a large bulge on its forehead and a dragon-like spiked frill.

74 Dinosaurs survived for 165 million years

People often think of the dinosaurs as being evolutionary failures, but they survived for a staggering 165 million years, far more impressive than the 200,000 years managed so far by humans.

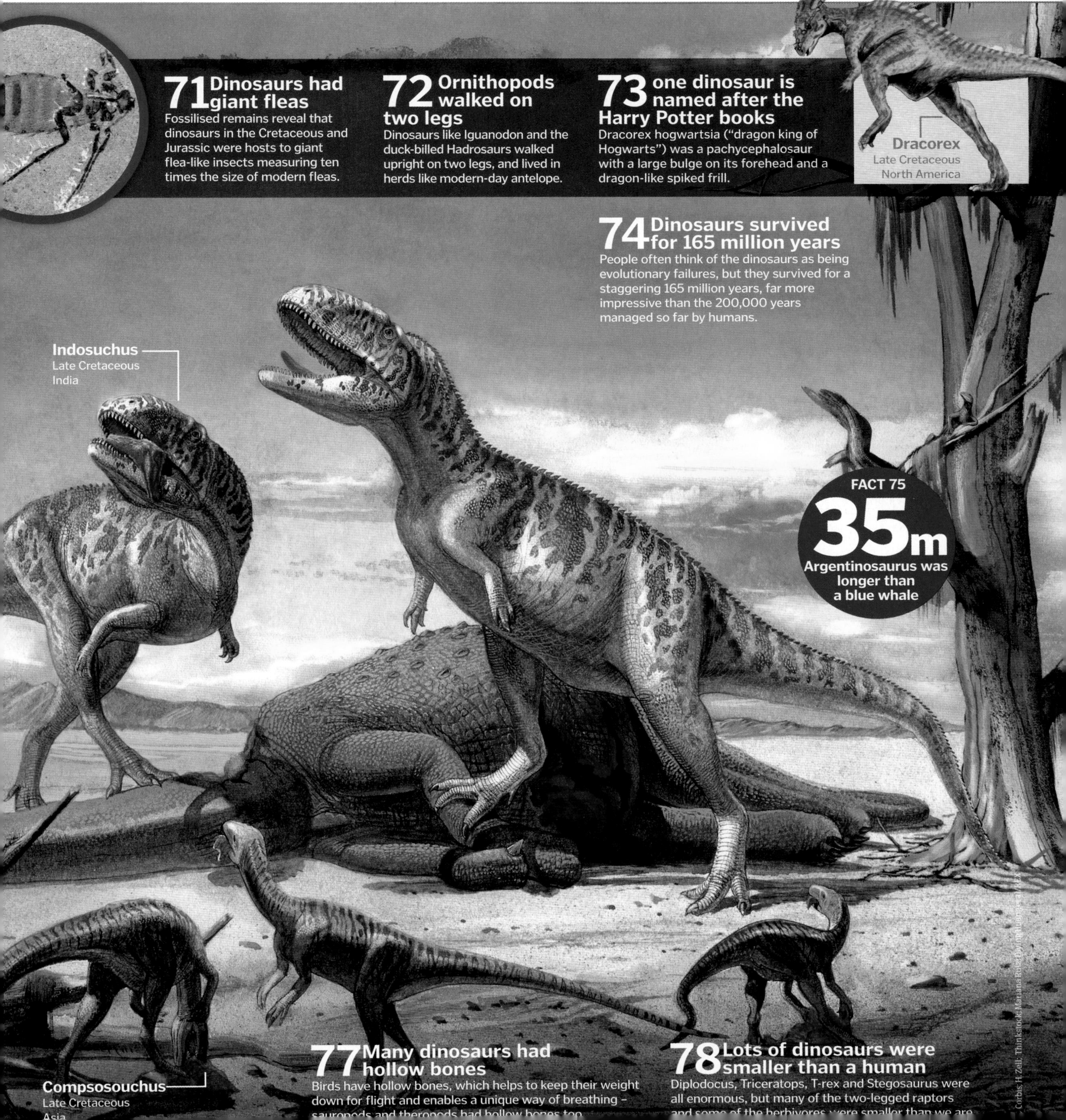

Dracorex
Late Cretaceous
North America
Indosuchus
Late Cretaceous
India
Compsosouchus
Late Cretaceous
Asia

FACT 75

35m

Argentinosaurus was longer than a blue whale

77 Many dinosaurs had hollow bones

Birds have hollow bones, which helps to keep their weight down for flight and enables a unique way of breathing – sauropods and theropods had hollow bones too

78 Lots of dinosaurs were smaller than a human

Diplodocus, Triceratops, T-rex and Stegosaurus were all enormous, but many of the two-legged raptors and some of the herbivores were smaller than we are

Hunting dinosaurs

Fossils have be found on every continent on Earth...

Ankylosaurus
Late Cretaceous
North America

79 North America has excavated the most dinosaur fossils

North America, Argentina and China have more than their fair share of dinosaur fossils. Areas with desert-type environments prevented the build-up of thick layers of plants, leaving the remains easier to find under sand and rock.

80 The first dinosaur fossil was found in England

The first dinosaur to be scientifically documented was Megalosaurus, formally named by William Buckland in 1824. The fossils were found in a quarry in Oxford.

81 Fossilised dinosaur highways allow us to retrace ancient steps

Enormous mudflats captured the imprints of dinosaur footprints, and some were preserved as fossils. Utah in the United States is particularly famous for its dinosaur trackways, which can be found on what used to be an ancient muddy floodplain.

JURASSIC COAST
South coast, UK

CLEVELAND-LLOYD DINOSAUR QUARRY
Utah, USA

82 New dinosaurs are discovered every year

There are hundreds of dinosaur fossils still to be discovered, and a new dinosaur is found and named approximately every seven weeks.

83 Chicxulub crater marks the asteroid impact that killed the dinosaurs

Chicxulub crater in Mexico is a 66 million-year-old, 180km (112mi)-wide impact created by a 10km (6mi)-wide asteroid. It is thought to represent the aftermath of the impact that killed the dinosaurs. In 2016, scientists plan to drill into the crater to learn more about its history.

CANDELEROS FORMATION
Argentina

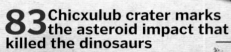

Giganotosaurus
Late Cretaceous
South America

84 Dinosaur bones can be recognised by distinctive skull holes

All dinosaurs have the same basic skull, with two holes for jaw muscles behind the eye and an air socket between the eyes and nose.

85 Dinosaur bones can be aged by radiometric dating

Carbon dating doesn't work on dinosaur bones, so scientists estimate the age of fossils by measuring radioactive isotopes in the surrounding rocks.

95 Dinosaurs weren't the first reptiles to rule the Earth

Around 300 million years ago amphibians dominated Earth, but as it got warmer, reptiles took over. There were pelycosaurs, mammal-like reptiles called therapsids, and archosaurs, from which dinosaurs, crocodiles and pterosaurs evolved.

96 Dinosaurs lived for up to 300 years

Paleontologists estimate the large dinosaurs had life spans ranging from 75 to 300 years. These estimates were made based on information we have on cold-blooded animals – warm-blooded creatures have shorter lives.

97 Troodons were probably the cleverest dinosaurs

Troodons lived around 77 million years ago and were about two metres (6.6 feet) long. They were carnivores, walked on two legs and had relatively large brains. They are also thought to be related to modern birds.

98 Amber insects don't contain dinosaur DNA

Jurassic Park is based on the idea that you could extract dinosaur DNA from blood preserved inside the bodies of mosquitoes encased in amber. Despite several attempts to recover DNA, it seems it doesn't actually survive inside the amber.

86 More than 100 different dinosaurs lived in Britain

Britain used to form a land bridge that connected Europe to North America, and has been described as a dinosaur paradise. It was home to over 100 different species, including armoured ankylosaurs, giant sauropods and three different types of fearsome tyrannosaur.

Megalosaurus
Mid Jurassic
Europe

87 There's no actual bone in a dinosaur fossil

When dinosaurs died, their bones were covered in sediment that was compressed and turned to rock. Over time, the bone itself dissolved away, leaving a bone-shaped hole in the rock, which then filled with minerals, forming a cast.

Diplodocus
Late Jurassic
North America

88 Most dinosaur fossils were found by amateurs

There are many more amateur fossil hunters than professionals, and they can cover much more ground. The largest T-rex fossil ever was found by an amateur.

89 There are two main types of fossil

Body fossils show the actual shape of dinosaur remains, while trace fossils show evidence of their lives, like footprints and nests.

FLAMING CLIFFS
Gobi Desert, Mongolia

BAHARIYA FORMATION
Western Desert, Egypt

FACT 90
77 tons
Argentinosaurus, weighed the same as a Boeing 737

ZHUCHENG
Shandong, China

91 Fossilised footprints tell us how they moved

Preserved dinosaur tracks revealed some theropods could run at 43.5kmh (27mph).

Iguanodon
Early Cretaceous
Europe, North America

LARK QUARRY
Queensland, Australia

92 Dinosaurs ran along riverbeds

Fossilised dinosaur tracks found in Australia reveal a superhighway where two-legged dinosaurs travelled on tiptoe through a fast-moving river.

93 The most ancient dinosaur fossils were found in Tanzania

One of the earliest-ever dinosaur fossils found is a 243-million-year-old dog-sized dinosaur called Nyasasaurus parringtoni. Bones from two different individuals were excavated in the 1930s, but weren't properly studied until 2012.

94 Dinosaur fossils are found on all seven continents

Dinosaur fossils have been found in the very northern parts of Canada, right down to the frozen wastes of Antarctica.

Utahraptor
Early Cretaceous
North America

99 Raptors had feathers

Of all the dinosaurs, the most feathery were the theropods. Velociraptors were covered in a layer of feathers, and so too was T-rex. Many other dinosaurs had spiny quills or feathery stubs.

100 Mammals used to eat dinosaurs

Repenomamus robustus was a 1m (3.3ft)-long mammal that lived approximately 125 million years ago. One specimen was found with dinosaur remains inside it.

101 Brontosaurus might have been a real dinosaur after all

Fossils were mixed up and the head of a Camarasaurus was placed on the body of an Apatosaurus. However, in 2015, a new study of the bones revealed that Brontosaurus has a longer and thinner neck than Apatosaurus and thus might be a distinct species after all.

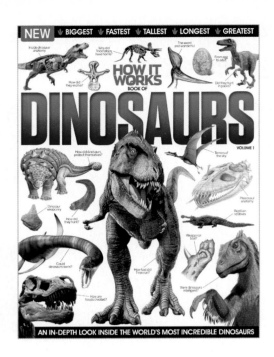

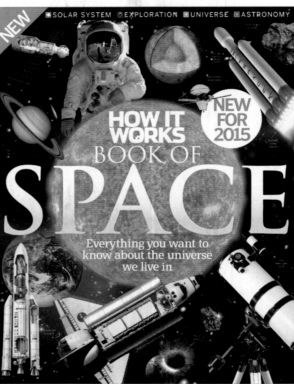
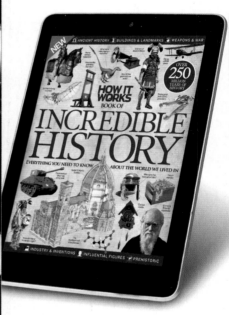